Yoga 4 Love

Tools for Mind, Body and Spirit

for a Holistic Lifestyle

By Lisa Ware

Yoga 4 Love: Tools for Mind, Body and Spirit for a Holistic Lifestyle

Copyright © 2018 Lisa Ware

Ordering Information

Quantity Sales and special discounts are available on quantity purchases by yoga schools, teachers, corporations, associations, and others.

Orders by U.S. trade bookstores and wholesalers please contact us: www.yoga4love.com or email: lisaware@yoga4love.com

Instagram @yoga4lovelisa .

Printed in the U.S.A.

Original Art and Digital Cover Art Design by Ashely Josephine Foreman

Headshot Photo Credit: Sweet Southern Artistry

ISBN: 9781513634920

Praise for

Yoga 4 Love Tools for Mind, Body, and Spirit: For a Holistic Lifestyle

Yoga 4 Love, Tools for Mind, Body, and Spirit is a wonderful journey into the science and practice of yoga in all its aspects, including right attitude and diet. Lisa Ware, in a clear and complete way, discusses all forms of basic yoga practice. At the same time in a very grounded way she delves into the deeper aspects of yoga related to the kundalini and energy bodies. A must read for all yoga practitioners and teachers.

--Jeff Migdow, Holistic M.D., Usui Reiki Master, *Prana Yoga Teacher Training,* Director

There is a tremendous new love flowing through the universe at this time. Miracles are flowing through practitioners at an accelerated rate these days, and Lisa is a pure channel for the grace you are seeking. I highly recommend this beautiful book to all who long to find truth in the name. Sat Nam. With Love,

-- Karena Virginia, healer and author of *Essential Kundalini Yoga*

Lisa is a true Goddess and sister, has seamlessly bridged yoga and holistic practices. Her personal practice, commitment and alignment with Spirit shines through in the integrity of her teachings. *Yoga 4 Love Tools for Mind, Body, and Spirit* is a book you must have in your library to find information, balance, the true teachings of yoga and more.

---Sierra Bender, author, *Goddess to the Core*; Founder, *Four Body Fit Institute* and Developer of the SBEM, Sierra Bender Empowerment Method

This comprehensive review of the philosophical principles of yoga is an essential teaching tool. It facilitates insight and understanding of complex ideas that's fundamental to all teaching of yoga.

--Kari Rollins D.O., The Wellness Center; ERYT 500

Be a part of the Yoga 4 Love Global Ambassador Goddess Tribe

#yoga4love #goddesstribe

@yoga4lovelisa

Tag a photo of you and your book to be featured on Instagram

Lisa Ware's Professional Offerings for deeper Study:

- *Yoga 4 Love's Big Book of Yoga Poses*, 101, 201 and 301 by Lisa Ware 2017. This eBook is a compliment to the book and your yoga practice. It is a comprehensive guide to the postures, benefits, contraindications and full color asana photos.

- *21 Days to Feeling Fit Guide Book*, by Lisa Ware 2018. The eBook for inspiration, the plan, the intention and the support.

- Yoga 4 Love Advanced Training Programs 200 Hour, 300 Hour Certification Online, Online Modules and Courses

- Reiki Healing, Trainigs, Shamanic Work and Angel Card Readings

- Free audio classes, meditations, workshops and handouts on the blog

- Life, Business and Health Coaching

- Yoga 4 Your Inner Goddess Retreats Texas

- Hawaii Yoga 4 Love Adventure Retreats

- YouTube channel LIVE STREAM, Video classes and Workshop Series on Lisa Ware Yoga 4 Love

- SoundCloud.com Audio Classes, meditations and workshops at Lisa Ware Yoga 4 Love

MIND BODY SPIRIT

Dedication

I dedicate this book to my mom and dad, who are both my angels now, and for the Highest Good in the Highest Frequency, as my offering for this planet, our true mother, Gaia.

Extra special gratitude to my loving, encouraging, patient, supportive family, especially to Richard my amazing husband, Aspen my beautiful daughter, Stoy my loving son, my sister Denise, and my Aunt Yvonne. In the spirit of Aloha, I feel so much appreciation to all of my extended family and friends, too.

I give infinite blessings for all of my yoga students, trainees, teachers, clients, yoga community, goddess tribe, supporters and followers.

I extend a deep bow to the seven directions and all of my crossed over grandparents and ancestors, my gurus, master teachers, Spirit Guides, Spirit animals, power animals and Reiki Master Teachers. I express infinite gratitude for the wisdom and teachings channeled through me, for the encouragement and messages of the angels and Archangels and for the teachings of Christ and the Great Spirit, the true I AM.

I dedicate my life to living on purpose, being present in the now moment with harmony and living my life through the Law of Attraction. I am in complete and total appreciation for the teachings and gifts brought through me.

Peace, Love + Light.

Special Acknowledgments

For my many helpful, encouraging and talented friends and Goddess Tribe ambassadors who held space for this book baby to be birthed, for the original painting done by my friend and talented artist Ashely Josephine Foreman upon inception of this idea many moons ago, who inspired the creation of the digital cover, and artist Sarah Farah for completing the digital cover and finally, to my awesome guide and Publishing Consultant, Brian Moreland.

For Cherry Flame

To the best 4 legged baby girl ever!

May we meet again at the Rainbow Bridge.

Foreword

Lisa Ware's Intuitive Vinyasa formats are intuitively adapted and downloaded from the Collective Consciousness and from connection to Divine Goddess. She has received inspiration many sources, from the teachings of Sri Ramaswami, the books and lineage of Krishnamacharya, the original teacher of Vinyasa Yoga. Lisa has deeply embodied the energy of Prana Flow® yoga with her guide, Shiva Rea and has received inspiration from many master teachers and gurus both living and crossed over. So much gratitude and a big curtsey to the great first lady of Western yoga, Indra Devi. Special acknowledgement is given to her mentor and sister, author and the original Goddess Warrior, Sierra Bender, international teacher of female empowerment. 'Goddess UP!'

Namaste.

Preface

In this book I have listed some ideas, many tools for you and important details on how to get started or intensify your daily practice. My hope is that you begin this journey, or deepen one you already have and continue to develop and share these practices daily until your life in this Earth realm is complete!

I am blessed to be able to write daily, this transpired after many years of putting time and energy into our three businesses. I am now able to live the life I dream; to travel, coach and teach, to host conferences, festivals and retreats and have my daily quiet time every morning with our horses and animals when I am at home. It wasn't always this way. We all start somewhere; I encourage you to you do what you can every day, to start now, to start today creating your dream life.

The first thing I ever did for a dedicated spiritual practice, now I know is called Sadhana, was simply to give up sugar for 40 days over Lent back in the '90's. The depths of my practices have definitely deepened, but my life's purpose and intention has always been to do the Sadhana, the deep work, to connect to something Greater than myself. Many of the tools I have acquired and learned are written here, in this book.

In this book you may see me using words interchangeably referring to something greater than our 'self'. To clarify, self with a small s, is referring to the human consciousness. The larger Self is written with a capital S and is also referred to as: Christ Consciousness, Prana (with a capital P), Divine, God/Goddess, Creator, Source, Mother Nature, Great Mystery, Goddess, Shiva, Shakti or Bhavana. There are so many names of Great Spirit! All are holy and respected equally. The way you refer to this energy is a personal preference and the names are all used to describe something that is omniscient of the Higher Self, which is infinite and directly connected to the Great I AM.

Peace, Love + Light;

Lisa

Table of Contents

Chapter 2

Chapter 3

Chapter 4

Chapter 5

Chapter 10

Introduction: Lisa's Story of Miracles

I was raised in a Lutheran household and I watched my Nana read her bible every night when I spent the night, and I knew was that church was a place to go on Sunday and sing, stand up, sit down and line up to go to the altar and get a sip of wine and a tiny round flat cracker. I was an acolyte, and went to youth group, but never really knew that I could know something greater, what the Lutherans called God, Christ, and The Holy Spirit. I never felt anything bigger than myself in that place of stained glass, beautiful walls; filled with the sound of voices and organs, smelling like candles and old lady perfume.

I grew up in Colorado, near Boulder with wonderful family memories of hiking, camping and spending countless hours in the mountains. My home life was the American dream and I am ever so thankful for my upbringing and my parents. There was a theme throughout my young life, as I sought out many ways to try to fit in. I did not have many good friends, or boyfriends, and low self esteem, despite my supportive family, so I turned to the pot smoking crowd. Luckily, before anything could take a huge turn for the worse my family uprooted us and set off to Texas. In 1986, I moved with my parents and little sister, Denise, at the influential age of fourteen from, and to say this was a culture shock is a massive understatement. I went from granola nature girl to suburban material girl, and yes, I loved Madonna and pop music. I found a group of friends in my neighborhood and my family found a local Lutheran church. My mom, dad and little sister attended regularly; I really liked to sleep in, so talked them out of going quite often. This was the special place, where unbeknown at the time, I would later get married to my amazing husband Richard at the young age of 20. I always enjoyed beauty, makeup and of course, as a child off the '80's I loved hair. And although I was a Colorado girl I learned to love big Texas hair. I tested out my beauty skills on my little sister; I even talked her into getting a perm to 'help' her curls. Then, I had her sit in the sun with conditioner (aka hydrogen peroxide). Her soft, smooth brunette hair quickly became like little orphan 'Annie, with a bright orange curly fro, and she was so mad! This was the sad beginnings of my interest in cosmetology.

1

At the time, as a teen, I looked to find people like me and I did. I found friends who were not involved in school stuff, like me, as unfortunately when I moved I had no counseling to direct me into school activities or sports. So, as a teen in high school I had a lot of free time. So I partied. I snuck out, smoked weed, went to the lake and drank, skipped school to go waterskiing and was tardy all the time so was regularly in detention. It was kind of like the movie The Breakfast Club in Saturday D Hall; fun but going nowhere fast. I tried a few activities and I loved Theatre, Speech and Drama. We had cars by then so I found that going to the club with a fake ID; and found dancing was my bliss. I went every night of every weekend, as often as I could and found myself on the dance floor all night, along with bad boyfriends, alcohol and stupid decisions. So I sought out fitness. In high school I joined a local gym, without my parent's knowledge and went to step cardio and dance classes as often as I could. I loved it! I even shaved the bottom of my hair off under my ponytail so I could get a better sweat.

It was soon thereafter at 19 that I started my yoga practice with a simple book of yoga poses with a gal in a leotard, marking and tagging all the pages, and making notes. I never went to a class or had a teacher; I just sought out what I needed that week and practiced it on my own with VHS tape on the VCR! And DVD's!. It was a simple practice, and I really did not think anything of it, and that is how my yoga asana practice remained until year 2000.

So I was back to square one, where do I go to find my bliss? I still went to the club, but began to really despise the smoky smell in my curly hair and I really thought most of the people there had such a gross vibe. I continued to seek and as I completed my high school education I also obtained my cosmetology license through vocational school. Immediately after graduation I began to work as a hair stylist and loved it! I spent one final summer with the party crowd until I met my soul mate. That day on September 23, 1990 my world shifted. We spend every waking moment together and I found bliss in true love.

We did everything together and we have together built a life of dreams, which we are living today, 28 years later. I write this introduction on a patio in Kona, Hawaii teaching a yoga retreat with him in paradise in 2017.

Immediately after graduation I began to work as a hair stylist and loved it! I spent one final summer with the party crowd until I met my soul mate. That day on September 23, 1990 my world shifted. We spend every waking moment together and I found bliss in true love. We did everything together

2

and we built a life of dreams, which we are living today, 27 years later, I write this introduction on a patio in Kona, Hawaii teaching a yoga retreat with him in paradise.

During the autumn of 1990 after meeting Rich, I quickly found an apprenticeship program in the hair industry and for the first time I found self motivated and excited people with dreams! I listened to motivational tapes and soaked it all up so quickly!! I loved listening to Zig Ziglar, Tony Robbins, Mary kay Ash. I really enjoyed networking meetings of enthusiastic and prosperous women! I went to the seminars and began to dream of my life and create vision boards. These skills stay with me to this day, and I am ever thankful for my friend Tina. She introduced me to Jesus Christ, as my first personal relationship to Spirit, in a praise and worship style church which she invited me to attend. I loved it and for the first time in my 19 years I felt Spirit move!!! I cried, sang, praised and we loved going to church together. I learned to have a relationship straight with Source, through Christ.

In May of 1992 Richard and I got married, and we were so in love. We honeymooned in Jamaica and began to build our life together. We moved to Dallas, Texas from a suburb apartment and I really loved the city! I still do love Dallas and continue much yogic SEVA (selfless service) community work in the DFW area hosting large events and teaching at festivals. We travelled and moved to a house and for five and a half years really enjoyed each other as newlyweds.

I moved up the ladder in the hair industry and got hired at a German corporation to teach hair color as an educator and platform artist. I loved the travel and the money, but not so much the corporate women. The energy with the co-workers was less that ideal. In February of 1996, Rich began his own business, and I supported us until it took off. Then I became pregnant in 1997 and knew it was time to leave the travel and corporate job in the hair industry. I went freelance as a hair color educator and platform artist and had also made a dedication to become vegetarian. I wanted to really live my life in a clean and healthy way, so left behind the toxic people in that corporate environment and the bad food decisions. When pregnant I knew that this was a time that I had completed 100% influence over my baby's health so I did my best to give my baby what was good. Rich and I went to birth classes at the local hospital and decided to do a natural birth.

Our first pregnancy was so exciting; we did not look at the sonogram gender because we wanted a surprise, yet I simply knew in my soul it a boy who was arriving. Yes, indeed it was a boy. We named him Richard Stoy

3

Ware III, and still call him Stoy, although now his Navy friends call him Big Daddy for fun. I do remember that I really loved Mexican food when pregnant with him, and to this day my son, who is now 19 as I write, thinks chips and salsa just may be a food group (true story)! He was a beautiful baby, with my green eyes and looked to me like a tiny little old man. He has a wise old soul.

The birth was lovely, no epidural, no drugs, no IV, and we used the techniques we learned at our Lamaze classes. I found something in the birth process, something like a bird flying above the ocean, it was my breath. My breath carried me through the turbulence of the labor pains, I watched the pains like the swell of the ocean waves, as an observer, I rose above the pains with my breath and I rode the pains like a pelican just above the surface of the water. I learned how to become the observer in that birthing room. My husband was an amazing guide and he had to shake me at one point to snap me back into my focus. He got so see both of our babies make their entrance into this world. I nursed both children for well into their second year. Our daughter was born in March of 2003, another beautiful natural birth, and we named her Aspen Rainne, Rich thought of her name and it was a perfect fit, naming her after the first trees that I fell in love with growing up in the Rocky Mountains of Colorado! We knew it was perfectly fitting, and to this day our daughter, now 14, is a shining bright light in our world. She is a natural born athlete and leader and we are so excited to see where her journey takes her.

I loved being a new mother, and this role is still the highlight of my Dharma, my life's purpose, although I always knew with an unquenchable passion there is more for me to accomplish in this world. I was totally granola before the word 'crunchy' was a thing. I made their baby food and froze it in ice cube trays, pumped and stored my milk so daddy could feed them and I could get a much needed break! I took them to playgroups, mother's day out and enjoyed staying at home with them. We lived in a primarily LGBT neighborhood and my baby boy, Stoy, had many new aunts, 'aunties' and uncles. We were a happy family. We still are today, and I am so blessed. In 1999, just before his first birthday we knew it was time to move from Dallas. We were thinking of the future, schooling and such, so we sought out my husband's best friend's dad who sold real estate.

In 2000, just after the New Year my mother went into the hospital and we thought she might not make it through the night. My mom had breast cancer in 1984, and I clearly remember as the oldest daughter being her

4

support team and watching her wash her hair in the sink as it all fell out. She had a mastectomy and her lymph removed from her left arm. We thought it was gone, and at the time had no idea about metastatic cancers. For 16 lovely years she raised her family, worked in Texas at a local airline headquarters and volunteered for a national breast cancer awareness organization. She made such a huge impact on thousands of women! She inspired men and women from her corporation to do 5K races and raise funds and awareness for breast cancer, and at the end of many of those 5K races she was asked to speak to the thousands of women in the pink hats, the survivors!!! Lorene Lydia Farrell was my mom ...and she was a survivor! We knew this with the depth of our souls. That day in 2000 when the doctors said that she will live through the night but that she had stage 4 metastatic cancer our worlds were rocked. Denise and I were in shock of the invasiveness of the treatment plan, the tubes, chemo, surgery, radiation and all the drugs were so against anything we believed in. We both sought out to our Source and asked for answers.

I found Reiki in that seeking. I told my mom about Reiki, and she was unfamiliar but open. It is a beautifully healing energy work practice that works straight through the Light of Christ Consciousness to bring the recipient, you, a loved one, a client, plants, animals, food, to a higher vibration. Reiki helps to connect mind-body-spirit and facilitates a sacred space held by the practitioner for the recipient and themselves to bring through whatever is needed in that now moment. My mom and I both went to Reiki level 1 and level 2 that year. The others in the classes held space for my mom's healing. For 7 years I practiced Reiki on myself, my family, my dogs, cats and various friends. My mom used her Reiki to go within and ascend the pain in her body, to help her in her quiet time, reading the Bible in her rocking chair; we both connected to Source and eachother through Reiki Distance Healing.

In 2007, I felt a calling. I wanted to do more with my life and although my Dharma as a wife and mother of two beautiful children was fulfilling I knew I had another purpose. With the inspiration of my mother, I watched how she tapped into Grace, kindness, humor as she handled her pain, her prognosis, her many diagnoses. She made the medical staff laugh and her many hospital rooms a party! She had a room full of people, balloons, plants and food and always laughter. I wanted to be like that, and remember that when her hair fell again we decided to have fun with it and so I cut her fine white locks into a Mohawk. She walked into the doctor's office with her hair

5

straight up with gel, and everyone was cracking up. I knew something was calling. I prayed to my Christ Source, and asked, and the immediate answer I got was yoga. Spirit said, in that still small voice inside my heart, *'yoga is what you have always went to you, it is your stillness'*. I knew that yoga was the answer to my seeking, it was true; I always turned to my yoga practice for my source of stillness, as I often found my life in a whirlwind of energy. I knew this was something bigger than me so I again asked what to call this and 'Yoga 4 Love' was the perfect Divine answer. So in 1997 it was named after my mom's positive inspiration. I searched for the name online to see what was open; it was available so I bought the domains. I immediately enrolled in a module based training that fit into my busy life...and so that is how Yoga 4 Love began.

Just before my second weekend of yoga teacher training my mom went into the hospital yet again, her body was frail but her spirit was as powerful as a lioness, as I clearly remember sitting with her watching game shows as she spouted off the correct answers. I brought her a little vial of grown grass from seed that I planted so she could smell it and a fossil from our waterfall creek bed. She was also still very sassy as I tried to arrange her flowers and fossil and she told me by pointing and making rude sounds with the thermometer in her mouth that told me that she did not like where I put these objects! We laughed with her at her motherly role, even from the hospital bed. I don't know why but I placed our left hands on top of each other and took a photo of our wedding rings, hand over hand. Before I was ready to go, I laid my head on her chest and said thank you to God and told her I loved hearing her heartbeat. She interestingly retorted, "Is is still beating?" and laughed. I said, "Yes... and I am so thankful." I said my goodbyes and told her I was off to my yoga training in Austin, and she kissed me, giving me her blessing. That was the last kiss from my mother. I came back just 3 days later to the hospital and Denise and my dad, Duane, told me mom had taken a decline but they did not want me to miss my training and so did not call me. They were used to her fighting, as she was a fighter. When they said she would not walk after hip surgery she said, 'Ill show you' and in a few short months she was out of the wheelchair. She said she had soccer games to go to and dance recitals to watch with the 2 grandchildren. This time was different, and I knew it as soon as I walked into the room. I actually knew it when my dad called me on the phone on my way home from Austin.

I went immediately to the hospital and locked eyes with my mother's pretty baby ocean blue eyes, as that was the only part of her body she had total control of. She looked into my soul and I rushed over to her. I kissed her and hugged her supine body and looked into her soul, through her blue eyes. I asked her out loud, "Mom, are you ready to go?" She hissed, "Yeeessssss," her blue eyes locked on mine. I told her it was ok, we would be ok and that she need not stay just for us, holding back tears. I told my dad in the hallway, and he said no, she is going to make it, and I said, as clear as a channel of Spirit as I had ever been to that day, "No daddy, not this time."

Just two weeks earlier her mom, my Nana, Lydia, passed. My mom was a fraternal twin and her twin died suddenly at 19, leaving Yvonne my aunt and Lorene. My mom had since vowed that her mother would never lose another child in her lifetime. Her mom was crossed over and she was reassured all was ok with the three of us, and she left her body within 3 days. I rushed over when I heard the news and called my pastor on the way Rich and I had joined an Episcopal church and when I called my pastor and told him what was happening. He in his wisdom, said, "What does that mean to you, Lisa?" I told him she was about to cross over and I wanted to ask him to be there for her last rites. He agreed and we arrived separately just after she died. My dad and sister were there already and we all gathered around her bedside, and held hands in a semi circle around her. For some reason I needed to see about her wedding ring, and it would not come off. So I left it on her finger and told the nurse to make sure to give that to my dad.

In our circle my pastor led the prayers and said the last rites as I found myself in my inner eye looking off to the upper left of her body. I saw a portal of Light!!! I saw a future come toward us, and then two figures! They were holding hands, it was Nana and Mom!!! They were waving!!!! I saw them go into the Light and then the prayer was over, and although we were all teary eyed I was in total JOY! I could not wait to tell them what happened! My pastor left, and Rich and Denise, her husband, my dad and I went into the waiting area. I really don't know what happened next but I did tell my sister immediately and this vision helped a little to ease the grief.

It felt like was the next day, but it was that same night that we went to my sister's house, since she was much closer to the hospital. What do you do when someone dies? We all were sitting around and then all of a sudden it struck me, I had my first real yoga class on the schedule, and it was May 7, 2008. It was a donation based community class (SEVA Karma yoga) and I thought 'oh shit how do I cancel this class, I don't even know who's coming!' I told Denise and she said 'no ma'am you are not cancelling', and gave me her yoga mat, some candles, some essential oils and threw me in the car. She said 'go teach!' And so I left. I arrived at the local karate studio where my son was studying to be a black belt, and there were so many moms there! I put down my mat and my problems for that hour. I taught, as a huge rain storm came in, thunder, lightning and rain for the entire class. No one in the class had any idea what was going on in my life, and I found that I was able to hold space for them throughout my grief and I forgot about me for that hour. I found power and pleasure and passion that night. I found my purpose, literally as my life turned a total 180 degree shift.

Since that night, the night my mom crossed over, it literally set in motion my life purpose, as well as my yoga teaching career. I have since lived my life to whittle away the part of me that is not connected to Spirit to be a clear channel of Light, and I have dedicated my life to serving others. The opportunities began to flow in an unexplainable, serendipitous way. I thought all over the rural area I lived, and desired to build a sustainable yoga community. I began my website presence with my website Yoga4Love.com, and began offering audio teachings online, too. I was offered a space to hold my classes, then over thanksgiving weekend 2010 was offered the studio ownership role. I again sought guidance and said YES to the Universe, without knowing the why or the how or the funding, and I trusted.

In December 2010 I sought out my sacred Reiki Master Teacher attunement. As the times were shifting again I began dedicating my actions and days to what my Source wanted to create in my life.

In 5 short weeks after deciding to say yes to the studio, on 1-1 of 2011 I opened my totally remodeled space as my first yoga studio, and it was a great success, we literally had a line out the door on New Year's Day! I really found my true purpose and began to pour my life's work into my teachings and my students and staff. Although the hours were long I loved being up at the studio. I invested in far infrared heat and laminate floors a few months into the ownership. I took up writing a lot and blogging. Through my practice and seeking as a student (as we are always a student in yoga) I met and found a dear friend and was invited to be a part of the Texas Yoga Association. I begin teaching annually at the Texas Yoga Conference. In 2011, at Texas Yoga Conference, as Spirit would align, I met another dear soul sister, Tania Wildbill, as my roommate at the presenter housing for the conference. She invited me to Oregon to teach at her Yoga Round Up, and now has partnered with me as co-creator of the Hawaii retreats!

2012 was a great year, the energy was really shifting in the Universe and many like-minded people felt that, as empaths and lightworkers. I made

8

a decision to become a life coach and did a year of mentoring with my guide and angelic teacher, Gary Quinn with Touchstone for Life. I began to deepen my work with the angels and the arch angels. My clairvoyance and clairaudience started to really come as a clear channel in Reiki and my guided meditations. Also, this was the year I developed my Yoga 4 Love Teacher Training manual and held my training in my studio. My training program had grown roots and was on its way to becoming what it is today, Yoga 4 Love Advanced Training Programs online, a global training program and destination retreats!

2013 came and my daughter turned 10, that year! I really dedicated my focus to healthy living and nutrition coaching with the Juice Plus company, in addition to my studio, as clean eating was a huge missing piece for my students. I held weekly smoothie parties at the studio to help my students develop a habit of healthy living. It was super transformational, and many of these people are now on my amazing team of wellness reps sharing nutrition all over the country! I really fell in love with helping people change their lives with this new found tool for health and financial freedom! Later that year my class of yoga trainees brached out to other states and we took our training online for the first time! I started recording all of my local and online classes for my training program, available at www.yoga4love.com/audio-video.

The next year a lot happened that changed the direction of my life in a total 180 degree shift. In the spring of 2014 Rich and I decided to make a decision to get a paint horse, and gifted him to our daughter for her 11th birthday, Cochise, who is about her same age. We added the second horse to our family 8 weeks later, a little filly just 9 months old, Diva. After I tamed her in the field; she kept coming to me in my dream realm and I knew she ws my heart horse. In April I went to Phoenix for a leadership conference. During that trip I spent a lot of time writing at the pool when I was not with my team. I basically downloaded an entire book from Spirit; title, cover, intro and table of contents.. This book is strangely enough a different book! The book that you are reading had to be completed first, as I will explain later!

In May, I was at a local Juice Plus community training with some of my friends and team members. I got a call that day. I was told my dad had esophageal cancer. I was in complete shock. Spirit again had placed me in a safe space, surrounded by my sisters to receive this devastating news. One of the ladies there was a nutrition coach and former osteopathic nurse and another in my small group had just finished her own chemotherapy. I vowed

9

to help my dad with all my tools and we quickly met with her and began a holistic treatment plan to compliment the Western medicine plan of 28 radiations and 5 chemo treatments. Over the summer he went to the nutritionist, tripled his Juice Plus whole food capsules, drank 2-4 plant based Complete smoothies and shakes a day and took the herbs the coach gave him based on the bio-feedback testing. He saw a Chinese doctor twice, whom came to us highly recommended, and his report was that his vitality was increasing, not decreasing, as normal chemo patients would expect! His doctors asked what he was doing, as he did not even lose his hair with Taxol (a super strong chemo).

On Labor Day, September 1, everything changed. We had a major house fire. I had just co-hosted two huge yoga festivals that I had been doing since 2008, DFW Free Day of Yoga, over Labor Day Weekend. I was at the studio preparing to host some Free Day of Yoga classes at my studio and at the front desk. I got a call on the studio line from my son. He said our house was on fire, and I was like, 'wait, what?'. Then he said, ' Just hurry home, mommy, it is only in the garage.' I had no idea what was going on, and I handed my studio key to one of my trainees who just happened to pop in. She said she would take care of the studio. I took off on my 12 minute journey home, which turns out you can reduce that to an 7-8 minute journey if you drive 70 in a 50. I just prayed so hard and so clear, asking God, what do I do? Spirit clearly said, 'get home but on the way post and tag all your loved ones on Facebook.' So I posted that my house was on fire while I drove. I know that is not the best choice, but I made it home in lightning speed, which seemed so long. I pulled up to the familiar long white gravel drive and saw the house smoldering from the already blackened roof. The scene was so surreal that I parked at the gate, halfway to the house, instinctively just pulled out my video on my phone and I started filming and narrating my thoughts while walking up, I stopped at the gate and my hubby was in the SUV in the middle of the land just watching in shock and horror. Three different fire departments were there, I believe is what he told me.. It started as an electric fire in the garage. My son, Stoy, discovered the fire, he said, 'I was on my computer and I smelt a burning smell. I remembered Aspen was making toast earlier, I checked the toaster, it wasn't that. The smell was still very strong, and I was curious to find out what it was so I opened the garage door.' When he opened the garage door he was blown back into the office by a back draft of flames. He immediately slammed the door with his foot and went to tell his dad and Aspen. He told them to get out; Rich had just laid down for a

10

holiday nap, so was disoriented, went into action, as his military Airborne Ranger training kicked in and went to fight the fire, leaving his phone and glasses in the bedroom. Aspen, only 11, had her robe on just after showering, and grabbed both a fourty and twenty pound dog under her arms and ran all the way to our closest neighbor's house. Luckily she did not stop to look for the three cats, Dusk, Cleo and baby Ming.

I did not see flames as I walked up in shock and surreal disbelief, but Rich and Stoy did; Rich had fought them with the garden hose to no avail until the volunteer firefighters arrived, but the fire, in his words, 'became alive'. It hit the insulation in the attic and he said it just began rolling. He knew at that point the house would not be saved.

Sadly, I greeted my dear beloved sitting on the back of the SUV parked in the middle of the pasture. We sat on the bumper helplessly watching the house smolder as several firemen worked diligently to save the home.

I saw a fireman come out the front door. He was holding my precious cat, Princess Cleo. She was completely limp, draped horrifically over his large arms. I said to Rich, 'I need to go to her!' He told me not to intervene, as they were doing their job. I was jut sitting there on the SUV; I could not obey. I ran over at full speed as he laid her on the grass, her super fluffy white fur, all matted, wet and full of black debris. She was glass eyed, staring into nothingness, panting, with her tongue straight out and barely getting any breath. She was about to cross over. I asked the fireman if I could take her and told him I was a healer. He gladly said yes, as he had much bigger issues on his hands. I yelled full force for my son. My son ran over. I dropped to my knees on the grass by Cleo and picked up her lifeless body, she was so light and limp. I began to pray and do Reiki for her and so did Stoy. We were barely able to see, and just at that time a lady firefighter came over with a kitty oxygen mask and a tiny bottle of O2!!! The mask was fitted to Cleo and she slowly and surely began to breathe. The oxygen quickly began to run out and I began to panic. The lady firefighter took me and the cat to the station; she came out with another bottle of O2. We somehow ended up in my neighbor's car, the one who was looking after Aspen. She drove us and dropped up off at the emergency animal hospital which was at least 40 minutes away, as we were in the country. The animal hospital would not see Cleo without a credit card! I was furious! I barely had shoes, let alone a payment, my neighbor gave them $100 to get the process started, and that was a huge stretch for her, she was so kind. Thankfully my sister was already rushing over and paid. They saved Cleo, and for that I am ever grateful. I had nothing left to do there so Denise, my sister and I left the pet hospital and drove home. I was beyond curious of what was left of it. When we arrived, the boys: my brother in law, Rob, Stoy and Rich, had taken some valuables out of the house and laid it all out on the grass. The house was a real mess, charred to the bare bones, totally drenched, and ceiling pieces all over the floor, basically it was inside out, and even though a structure remained it would have to be totaled. All of the contents that weren't melted or charred were wet and coated with a black sticky tar 1/16 inch thick. It was so, so sad to see my life, all our stuff, just ruined.

After the hubbub of people died down and the sun began to set my family had to decide where we were going to stay. My sister in law offered, so Rich took the family over there. I luckily had a few tank tops from my event that weekend in my yoga bag, so at least I had something to wear. I stayed at the house in my car with one of my yoga trainees who came over in support. She and I were talking and at sunset she sent me love and pulled away. I drove off just after and as I was leaving the long white gravel drive, pulling away from my known life and familiarity, I had an unknown peace upon me. I paused just outside the gate. I stopped and asked, "God, Lord, Creator, Spirit, why do I feel at peace?" The Universe clearly and immediately responded, *"Child, this is your time to receive."*

We did not know where we were going to live or what was going to happened or how we were even going to provide for our children with clothing and shoes, but we just trusted in something greater. My best friend, ever true and faithful, came in town to help me salvage through the wreckage that was my old life. In October, the house still sat exactly as it did on September 1, but now everything was molded and the house filled with mosquitoes. In the rental home, out of necessity, I began to stream live yoga classes and record my Yoga 4 Love Advanced Training Program with my trainees live online. I also learned how to be still, use mantra, meditate and do self care to really go within during this time in my life.

At one point I was so disoriented in my life, so unrooted. I closed my eyes in a nice hot shower in the rental house; I opened them and had no freaking idea where I was. I then quickly realized my reality and just sobbed and sobbed. After Cleo was better and cat sitting was finished from my dear friend and heart sister, Sarah, she came to live in my rental home's lovely walk in closet. I spent a lot of time in there snuggling on the floor under the donated clothes. She slept on my head.

I began seeking spiritual teachers, I thought I needed a teacher here on Earth, as almost all of my teachers and guides had been crossed over already. I got wrapped up in some misaligned energy and really went down a path of some really strange and dark meditations. I had somehow come way off base from my Christ Source and never ever again will I wander from the Truth.

In October, 2014, I had a trip planned to Memphis for the next Juice Plus conference, and so I decided to go. I just needed to get away. The weekend I was to leave the insurance company finally declared the portions of the home that were not salvageable to be demoed. I got to swing the sledgehammer and bust up my old bathroom tile, boy that felt so good. I really wanted to tear up that 1978 kitchen, and took the sledgehammer to the laminate countertops. Not a damn budge! It literally bounced off. I worked to at least make a dent in the kitchen demo working up a huge sweat. Another great thing was that I was already scheduled to leave town, so I left as the really hard emotional part started. That was when the guys started ripping items out of the attic, all melted, destroyed and charred. I saw my childhood and my kid's Christmas ornaments fall into the piles of muck and black mess, ruined, saw my kids photos fall out and lay on the ground. It was just too much. I lost it. In front of the entire crew I had a total melt down, throwing anything, cursing, and crying. My neighbor, David, had joined the crew and was a great support in perspective, friendship, photo documentary and humor throughout the entire process.

During the undertaking, we were able to save the foundation of the house and rebuild our dream house on the exact same foundation, overlooking the stone canyon waterfall that we love so much.. I wanted a new kitchen for over a decade, and now the Universe was granting me my dream kitchen and we did not have to be in debt to do it. Now here is something to ponder: years earlier my friend, Sue and I had created my dream house plans over weekend nights of wine and fun on auto cad, as she was a structural engineer. I suddenly remembered these plans when we began the demo process. I looked up the files on an old cloud file. The insurance company deemed to demo the entire structure, except for the exterior studs and the interior studs surrounding the three old bedrooms. The plans we had created all those years ago, and the walls we wanted to keep LITERALLY totally matched the exact layout of the parts of the house that were salvageable. The parts the insurance company wanted to salvage were the same walls and the roofline that Sue and I kept on our original blueprints of our dream house! We were able to pick up these plans and immediately give them to the builder with only one edit! You just cannot make this stuff up!

I began to totally realign my life to bring everything back into foundational only items, in total obedience to Spirit. I knew something had to go, as my life was in complete chaos, and the energy of Kali Ma and I became really familiar. I closed my yoga studio. I was told clearly to focus on bring everything back to center; this when my teacher training students began to come to me virtually.

In late October I met my 'brain coach'. He works on emotional impact and when he called me out in front of the room and asked me what my goals were, I could only stammer out what I did not want. He told me some things that made me realize that I was not teaching from a firm foundation ...and I was so mad at him!!! For a month I was mad, until I realized that he was right. I surely did not want to be the next motivational speaker or some ethereal teacher that is all hype and love, leaving people in a high state of bliss to go out into the world with no substance and be dropped off into reality. I wanted to teach from Truth, traditional teachings and straight from Spirit. I rewrote my training program based on lineage and real truth and history, not just feel good yoga bliss and bullshit kick your asana classes. This forever has impacted the content and direction of the material I teach and write.

November came and for a year I had a booked out a weekend Goddess workshop planned with one of my mentors, Sierra Bender. When she and I spoke she was surprised to hear that I thought the show must go on! We had over 30 women attending and I was surely not going to cancel on them. It turned out to be an amazing and beautiful, magical weekend.

I spent the next few months in chaos, destruction and then manifestation, while learning to live in the energy of Kali Ma. Kali destroys but she also creates beauty from destruction. I felt like the Phoenix, rising from the ashes of my old life. I had even recorded a Phoenix rising meditation in August 2014, to later realize that this meditation was also meant for the future me.

In December of 2014, on complete faith, Rich and I bought a large cabin, a roughed out shell, and had it moved into our property on the waterfall. We had Sue help with the plans to convert it to the now Yoga 4 Love Cabin Studio, retreat center and my husband's man cave. We finished it out at the same time we were building our house, even adding a full bath!

14

We moved back into our brand new dream house, according to the architectural plans we created years and years earlier. It was March 2015, on my daughter's 12th birthday that we moved in. She, her best friend and I spent that first night on a pallet in the new home! We moved in that week, Stoy, Rich my cat Cleo and my two dogs. They had mated in the rental house, and had 3 sweet puppies a week later, in my master closet. I was midwife to the puppies for my sweet Cherry Flame. One was born still, and we named him Angel, and buried him on the property. It was full circle, we lost our kitten, Ming in the fire, and now as we came back to the land, a puppy gave his little life. We did a house blessing and placed crystals on the points under the foundation and began to rebuild our home.

Dusk had remained on the property as guardian, Prince Dusk, as he is Cleo's offspring, born on this land. He stayed over the entire winter, one of the coldest and wettest of many winters, with only a cat tree in the barn with a sleeping bag over it. When we moved back in and brought Cleo back, they reunited in the hall and both of them immediately went to the exact spot on the floorplan where we found Ming when he died! They sniffed the area, although it was totally remodeled, they knew. Then as quickly as it came, they moved on.

My dad's dis-ease continued to digress. If only he had the belief to continue the nutrition protocol that was working! He had been in the rehab center or hospital since October, when he decided to let the surgeons cut on his tumor. The body can only take so much and 7 short months later he passed. It was May 1, 2015, Beltane, that old Celt! He went to the other side while holding my hand, as I helped him cross, in the path of the Shamanic Practitoner, with my sister by our side. I felt his spirit leave his body, as he exhaled the longest exhale I have ever witnessed. I sang the HU as his spirit lifted out of his body. Again, life took yet another deep turn. He was interred next to my mom at Dallas-Fort Worth National Cemetery with a veteran's flag ceremony on May 7, 2015 which was seven years to the day that my mom crossed over. Like I said, you just can't make that stuff up. The serendipitous moments and the full circle timelines just show me over and over that my life is totally orchestrated by something much greater than we are, as is all of ours, if we only look for the miracles. Later that month my hubby and I celebrated our 25th wedding anniversary and it was another bittersweet moment in time.

In September on my 43rd birthday in 2015, I became an ordained minister thought the Universal Life Church Monastery, and intentionally

15

dedicated my life over to the will of Spirit. At the end of 2015, after living on the sacred land we bought in 1999 for 16 years minus the time we were at the rental home, we paid off our bank note and our brand new dream home is now ours!

In 2016, I continued diligently to work on my yoga training and completed my online recordings for the 200 hour certification and the first draft to my Yoga 4 Love manual online. In May of 2016, my son graduated high schoolIn 2017, I began to study as a Shamanic practitioner. This year had culminated five years spent writing and the completion of my training program and my website.

In February, again, my life took another major turn. In July of 2015 our son had enlisted in the US Navy, qualified for the Nuclear Engineering program, and went into a waiting program called DEP. He was at the time 18, and had been waiting almost a year in the DEP (delayed entry program). When he was called to go in February he was ready. He went off to boot camp in Great Lakes, Illinois, along with a major portion of my heart chakra. I was so very proud; it was bittersweet. I was at a huge loss with my only boy out of the nest so suddenly, and now government property to boot. I did a card reading for myself using a deck that had many Native American teachings. The card I drew for the question of whether my son would be safe in the US Navy was the 'Cradle Board'. The Universe confirmed that my son was covered by ultimate protection and pure love. The cradle board was used on the back of the papoose where the baby was swaddled to keep him protected at all times. I was totally at peace, and in complete Trust with this much needed answer from God.

The next 9 weeks were super hard. I was in the midst of finishing the new website, doing uploads of hundreds of hours of recorded classes on audio and video, which was a huge highlight, but my heart ached so hard that I could feel a space the above my high heart that was totally void. It was missing. I fell into a deep sadness that was congruent with the time he was in boot camp. I have never been depressed, but can not empathize with those who have. I cried myself to sleep almost every night, burst into tears randomly at the stoplight; I cried for loss of the dad, missing my mom, every bit of grief just seemed to come out; I cried for my cat, I cried for my past home. Our family dynamics shifted, and it was just the three of us at home and I felt like I honestly lost my best friend along with my son leaving the nest. Aspen had a hard time too, and as a teen she had to navigate a place without contact with her big brother. Rich had some comprehension of what to expect as he was in the service, too. He served in the US Army in the 82nd Division as an Airborne Ranger, and thankfully so, because he was and still is my rock.

In April, we finally had a call or two from our son and he started to receive letters. At the end of the month we flew to Chicago to see him graduate. For all of you military moms out there, you know because you're a part of this sisterhood. For the rest of you that have not ever experienced a child in the military, I will summarize it to say that their Graduation ceremony is the biggest most pride filled and beautiful experience. Words cannot express how it feels like to see your child achieve such a massive goal. Although I was aching inside yet another sign was so clear to me from Spirit that he was on the right path. This was the packing process; as he had packed up his room before he left for bootcamp it came full circle, we literally unpacked the remaining few boxes in the attic that had held the restoration items from our fire three years earlier. He used these same boxes to pack up his items, as he 'sailed' off to become a man after bootcamp for Nuclear Engineering Training in the Navy.

I felt relief as he was on his path, and continued to pour myself into the completion of the content for my book, finalizing any tweaks on the online training program on my website and scheduling upcoming retreats. In September of 2017, on my 45th birthday, we launched the entire 200 hour training program the Yoga 4 Love website and we enrolled so many new students that day!

Just after my birthday, over the autumnal equinox, Richard and I held our first yoga retreat with a dear friend Tania from Oregon, the friend from 2011. It was not only a yoga retreat but a 25th anniversary bucket list vacation on the Big Island of Hawaii.. We brought our daughter and we all totally fell in love with the island. We celebrated and incorporated the festivities into our time together. We spent the actual anniversary of the day we met 27 years earlier with the lovely people from our yoga retreat, and then went hiking in the Volcanoes National Park. I was so honored to be in the presence of Goddess Pele. We experienced some really major shifts and transformations and made an intention to set our life in motion by making a major life decision. We bought a deed in Hawaii with intention to host regular retreats, spend time on the Big Island of Hawai'i and to travel the world together. We are so thankful that we are guided so clearly on our way by the Universe into this 'OMAZING' lifestyle. We invite you to join us on this journey!

Author's Intention

I have spent six years writing, which started for my yoga training program writing to fulfill a need for a manual. As the program and my offerings morphed to an online platform I began to totally let go of the outcome and alow this process to simply be, and to continually listen to Spirit. As we come into this final stageof this phase, it is to be complete with the creation of this book. I have invested much time and energy creating, recording, videoing and writing. These tools, teaching and offerings are for you! I want you to find your passion, your purpose, and the time and financial freedom to do what you love. I desire for you to have a deep, unwavering connection to something greater than yourself, to know Spirit and to experience miracles daily!

I desire to continue to be a clear channel, that any and all teachings that Spirit gifts to me may become available and tangible, so that anyone in the world can learn and utilize these life teachings from anywhere on the planet. Please, be my guest, enjoy the book and share it with others that may be on your heart. I have placed much information in this book, on my website, www.yoga4love.com, and on my YouTube channel, Lisa Ware Yoga 4 Love. Feel free to also take some free classes with Yoga 4 Love online!

If you would like a deeper study, perhaps one of the many online course studies may be a perfect fit for you. If you choose to deepen your yoga journey with us, you may want to take a specialized training module or even earn a 200 or 300 hour yoga certification through our online courses. If a retreat getaway with your like minded Tribe is more your style, perhaps we will spend time together one day at one of our Yoga 4 Your Inner Goddess Retreats in Texas, at a Hawaii Yoga 4 Love Adventure Retreat or on a future destination vacation!

What is Intuitive Vinyasa?

The material written is conglomerated from eclectic sources. As I have written them I have put my personal signature on each topic to teach what has worked for me, my clients and students. I have meditated and asked many questions. I have developed this style of yoga and it all began in 2007, with my first class the day my mom crossed over, teaching straight from the heart. I have thus far taught between seven to eight thousand hours by 2017 and recorded hundreds of hours of the teachings. These sequences were adapted from the linear vinyasas of the past and downloaded straight from Spirit. I recorded all my classes live, then written the sequences onto a legal pad, then wrote them into the manual, and sequentially into this book.

I have inquired to Spirit what makes these teachings different. Why were the tools downloaded by me and why do I feel this huge need and call to write, record and post to get the tools out in the world? In clear and immediate response to my inquiry to the Universe, Spirit told me that these yoga teachings are called Intuitive Vinyasa. It is exactly that. These yogic teachings are the traditional teachings available for the 21st century, adapted to the Divine Feminine, as the Goddess energy is a very present and active Source in the current day and time.

I asked what makes this teaching different than what our masters have taught? The yoga trainings within are solidly grounded on the teachings of Vinyasa, in the lineage of Krishnamacharya with personal mentoring by Shiva Rea and Sri Ramaswami. I have consulted with master gurus in books by BKS Iyengar, Desikachar and many other master teachers. I asked why I needed to publish this material, and the following is what Spirit had me write, no edits.

What Makes the Yoga 4 Love Teaching Method Unique?

Intuitive Vinyasa is:

a yoga practice or class taught with the traditional elements of a vinyasa flow, the movement of Prana, the connection to Source and the mindfulness of being present with and for our Self and the ones whom we are teaching.

Intuitive Vinyasa is also:

the ability to utilize the tools of Yogic truth (Sat) and bring these teachings intuitively into the present now moment, with relevance to the mind-body connection. It is a way of life, moving with the breath, using the body as an expression of art, and a deep personal connection to Spirit. Trainees learn to practice with energy, the elements: Earth, Water, Air, Fire, and Ether, as well acknowledgement of the four directions, our ancestors and our lineage.

Your Personal Journey

As you read, take what you need, table the rest until you need it or until you serendipitously meet someone who can use it. The tools here are free to use and share, all I ask is that when you do you honor the source.

As I sit here and tell you my story I am on the big magical Island of Hawaii, looking out at coconut palms and infinitely expansive skies to the mother Ocean beyond. I am standing firm on the black lava land of Goddess Pele, as a reward to being an obedient servant to the Source. I think often of you, and want you to have the biggest, most OMAZING life that you can lead. Through this life, living out loud, may you bring through your gifts and talents to the world!

The reason the book has come about is because Spirit told me to reach global. This book is available for everybody in the world to enjoy. With that I have no attachment to the outcome.

If you read on and are inspired, join our mission! Our Yoga 4 Love motto is *Expanding Horizons, Inspiring Positive Change.* If you are ready for transformation in your life, please apply these tools written here. Simply apply them as you go, using the teachings as a personal coach. There is no need to read through the book in order, or cover to cover. These teachings have been downloaded by me, through Source, for you.

Use the book as an oracle, opening the book randomly, flipping to the topic of what you need that day. This technique is called 'Wehe i la Paipala' in Hawaiian.

Many of these teachings have deeper assignments, or take one of the many audio and video practices available on yoga, breath work and guided meditation. Many free resources are up on our website at

21

www.yoga4love.com. Visit there, as well, to download all the supplements to this book including all of the yoga poses from my manual available in my free eBook: *Yoga 4 Love's Big Book of Yoga Postures; Asana 101, 201 and 301* in PDF.

Connection is where we make this world OMAZING. I invite you to please connect with us directly through the website or find me on social media @yoga4lovelisa.

For a personal connection schedule a free video chat coaching session with one of our Directors on my website www.yoga4love.com! There is space for you to plug right in today to the global Yoga 4 Love online community online, through the like-minded Facebook group Yoga 4 Love Global Goddess Tribe, or go deeper through learning Reiki, personal life or holistic health coaching, in our Advanced Training Programs online or at one of our upcoming retreats.

Namaste.

Lisa's Mission

My personal mission is to bring light, love, clarity and oneness through my right actions, to manifest abundance and live in alignment with Spirit.

Through time, dedication and obedience I have learned to be still, listen and go within to hear the Goddess in my heart. Through these teachings I continue to bring the ancient teachings of Vinyasa yoga, to download and record them with a feminine Shakti goddess twist, making these teachings not only available online but also in tune with our Mother planet, Gaia, for the 21st century. All of the teachings here in this book have been credited to the sources and the lineages to the best of my ability. The yoga sequences given to me by Spirit have been directly brought through, taught, recorded then written here for you.

We are so stoked that YOU are a part of this movement, through the Yoga 4 Love online community you may engage in many ways through the tools we offer. We are gaining momentum all over the globe and spreading love from from woman to woman, mother to child, partner to partner, and student to teacher, as our master teachers have taught!

In this day in age we are utilizing *'Spirit through Technology'* reaching people all over the world, making the TRUE teachings available 24/7/365! We need you to on this mission! Together let us share truth, light and love!

Yoga 4 Love Vision Statement

We offer a sacred space for women to build a tribe in community with other like-minded sisters from all over the world. We create a safe and open place where women meet virtually, energetically and in person, facilitating healing, happiness, adventure and joy using the tools of yoga, whole food, meditation, Reiki and energy work.

Chapter 1

Intro to Yoga, Pranayama, Bandhas, Mantras 101

Sadhana is a discipline undertaken in the pursuit of a goal. Abhyasa is repeated practice performed with observation and reflection. Kriya, or action, also implies perfect execution with study and investigation. Therefore, sadhana, abhyasa, and kriya all mean one and the same thing. A sadhaka, or practitioner, is one who skillfully applies...mind and intelligence in practice towards a spiritual goal.~ B.K.S Iyengar

Sadhana, An Introduction to Daily Yogic Practice

I would love to begin by sharing with you a little about what part of my practice has made the most impact in my life. You may think we are referring to yoga asana, or the poses. Although the postures are freeing and challenging, and have unlocked some special doorways for me, it is my Sadhana, or yogic daily rituals, that have been the most significant part of my positive transformation.

Sadhana is the daily practice; it is what fuels our development as a yogi and as a human being, while living a hundred or less years on this beautiful planet. This practice is not something to check off a list, and it is very different than asana or meditation. Sadhana is done with specific intention to grow and awaken to the Flow.

There is a common saying, "You are what you eat." In yoga, there is another saying. "Your habits define you."

Kundalini Yoga recognizes every soul as perfect, pure and divine. There is nothing to redeem or purify at the soul-level, isn't this great news!? The soul is complete and beautiful as it is. But this reality "life" is based on our habits. Our habits define us to ourselves and to other people. By our habits, we live in peace, joy and happiness. By our habits, we create suffering and pain. When we change our habits, everything around us can change. For many years I held a forty day spiritual practice over Lent (a 'sadhana', as I now know it). The first thing I ever did for a spiritual practice was simply to give up sugar for 40 days. The depths of my practices have definitely deepened, but the intention is always to do the Sadhana as an intention to connect to something greater than ourselves. Read on to learn more.

In this article I have listed some ideas for you and many important details on this topic to get you started on your daily practice. My hope is that you begin this journey, or deepen one you already have and continue to develop this practice daily until your life in this Earth realm is complete!

You may ask, 'what is this sadhana thing anyway?' Well, a sadhana is simply a daily spiritual practice designed to allow oneself to turn inward and perceive life as it truly is. [1]

You may also be thinking, 'I'm not religious at all, why would I want to do a spiritual practice?' If I may answer, just in case you asked; being spiritual is not about religion at all – although it might mean you have a personal relationship to God, the Divine, the Universe, the Infinite, Consciousness, Allah, the Divine, Source, The Great Mystery, Spirit, Goddess, Shiva, Shakt. Whatever word you like to use to describe something that is omniscient is perfect. Many people find connecting with nature is an innately spiritual experience; it makes them feel more in tune with life, and with themselves. A spiritual practice is simply a practice that connects you to your Highest Self. That is – your ego self, which is small, limited and

---

[1] Alan Verdegraal, "Tantra: The Magazine", Issue #8, p22-23 Copyright 1994

separate from everything else, to your Higher Self, which is infinite and connected to the great I AM.

Here are some ideas for a daily of 40 day Sadhana:[2]lighting a white candle daily, saying a mantra, doing a chant, practicing a specific daily meditation or a specific yogic asana practice like surya Namaskar, sun salutations; this is a set yoga practice which can include asana (poses), pranayama (breath work), meditation, mantras, chanting, mudras (yoga for the hands) and other yogic practices, practicing creative visualization, saying daily affirmations, with intention, reading a spiritual text, or taking a daily walk in nature.

Why do we practice a sadhana for forty days?

A sadhana doesn't have to be for forty days, it may be just every single day for an indeterminate length of time, or it may be a set time that you decide. Forty days is usually the minimum, it's a number with significance in many spiritual texts, including the Bible, as Lent is for forty days. One reason for this is when you do something every single day for forty days, it ingrains the new discipline into our brains; this is the study of neuroplasticity! The grooves in the brain get re-grooved or *REALLY GROOVY*! These new grooves (sadhana) can replace old bad ones (samskaras) and this literally now becomes part of who you are!

What are the benefits of practicing a sadhana for forty days?

SELF LOVE! Love your self. LOVE YOUR SELF. No one can ever love you more than you. This is the calibration for all other love to come in.

---

[2] http://theyogalunchbox.co.nz/what-is-a-sadhana-and-why-do-i-need-one-in-my-life/

Ebb and Flow, baby! This is the cycle of giving and receiving. Commitment ~ a sadhana may only be one, three, five or ten minutes a day, but just doing it every single day no matter what says that you care about your spiritual evolution. Put yourself first. Do not cancel on you, do this regularly and you are growing and evolving.

Discipline ~ the ego is shrewd, clever and tricky. It and will use all kinds of excuses to try and keep you from doing your sadhana. Doing it every single day builds discipline as we learn not to listen to the mind and the ego, and to just DO what feels good because we know we truly want it. Every thought that feels good is bringing us closer to our Inner Guidance System and attracting more feeling good thoughts!

Evolution ~ you're either changing or growing as a person, or you're stagnating. "When you rest you rust", said the women's movement entrepreneur, Mary Kay Ash. Do you want life to imporve? Doing a daily sadhana is one small way to make sure that every single day is just a little bit better than the last one, no matter what else is going on in your life.

Foundation ~ in just 1-10 minutes. A sadhana is like planting a tiny little seed in the garden. Every day you practice you water it and it grows... and as you get used to dedicating ten minutes a day to your evolution and growth, you'll naturally discover you want to create more and more time for yourself! That tiny seed blossoms, grows and bears fruit and one day you turn around and discover your whole life has become a sadhana. (read more about Sadhana in the book *BE HERE NOW*, by Ram Dass)

I want to start my own Sadhana. How do I start?

Set an intention based on one aspect of yourself you want to evolve, or what aspect you'd like to let go of. Find a practice that supports that, there are ideas to follow.

Want to open your heart and increase the amount of compassion you feel for yourself and other people? Try a heart opening yoga practice. Want to find greater mental clarity, increase your intuition and open your third eye? Try a simple OM or chant meditation. Want to get rid of old mental and emotional behavior patterns? Try a chakra balancing, crystal healing or Reiki practice. Want to build a daily yoga asana practice? Practice surya namaskar (sun saluations) every single day, starting with five a day and building up to 30 a day or more.

Want to be a part of something greater? Go to a Global Mala [3] yoga event, which is happening around the world every fall on the Autumnal Equinox, September 20th and 21st. Many local yoga teachers also host a Global Mala sun salutation practices, look online!

For those who want to seriously practice deep cleansing actions for the mind, body and Spirit, it is time to formulate a specific Sadhana, a cleansing action called a Kriya. The result is accelerated spiritual evolution. Sadhana becomes a powerful method to achieve this result. See a master yogi or a holistic health care practitioner to prescribe you a specific kriya. Talk to a spiritual leader, Ayurvedic doctor or advanced yogic practitioner to help you choose an appropriate kriya, chant/mantra or pranayama. Practice your special kriya, chant or mantra every single day for the same amount of time.

---

[3] www.globalmala.com

There are three important aspects of sadhana:

1. Choice
2. Commitment
3. Aspiration

The first stage of sadhana is to choose a practice. Even the simplest sadhana will be challenging to the newcomer. Consider this simple sadhana of lighting a candle every night, then immediately blowing it out; nothing more or nothing less. Do this for ninety days. You will observe the mind coming up with every reason why you shouldn't do it and every excuse why you missed a few (or many) nights. Yet by accepting it as a sadhana, you make a choice to do it and it becomes a spiritual practice. I find that when I don't want to do my nightly meditation and just want to fall into bed that I can do this simple Sadhana. It keeps me on track and I know that by this simple act I am growing spiritually.

The second aspect of sadhana relates to regularity, doing something at periodic, planned intervals. This typically would be at the same time in the same place everyday. Yet it doesn't have to be everyday. This sadhana practice could be every other day or every Tuesday and Thursday, as long as it is regular. Doing practice irregularly is not sadhana. Once the schedule is selected, the challenge of sadhana is to stick with it and not to miss your own appointed time. This is the first measure of commitment, commitment to your Self time. This creates a strong sense of self worth and discipline.

The third measure is to make a commitment for a specific period of time; that is, choose do the practice for thirty days, sixty days, ninety days, 108 days or even 1008 days. Notice the level of your success, and then take a break. It may seem like you can keep going, but it is wise to break then recommit. Decide upon another practice (or the same one) and make another

30

commitment, or add onto your already established practice. Choice and regularity are not the only aspects of sadhana. If they were, getting dressed or brushing our teeth every day would be a sadhana. We choose what clothes to wear and we do it. Brushing our teeth could be a sadhana, yet it is most often just a mechanical action done everyday, however everything shifts once we set this simple act as Sadhana and dedicate it to our spiritual practice.

The final key to a successful Sadhana is setting your conscious intention. This is where the power of the Source, Prana with a capital 'P', and the Universal life force is generated! This moment is when the intention becomes an aspiration.

Many yogis chose a simple action, the practice of using a neti pot, the washing of the nostrils with distilled water mixed with Himalayan salt. For this to be a sadhana, however, rather than just another cleansing action like washing the body in the shower, your intention is necessary.

With these words not only is an intention created around the practice, but an aspiration for each day. You will gradually become more consciously aware of having a spiritual goal. Perhaps your ultimate goal is Samadhi, bliss with Creator and becoming a spiritually enlightened being, awakening to the Truth. Setting an intention is required to keep it from becoming mechanical or something that you check off the to do list. Initially, it will challenge the mind and the ego, and even your schedule

Simple statements to help set intention to do your Sadhana practice:
- This simple act is all I have to do to evolve spiritually.
- This is the only practice that I must do to spiritually grow.
- This is the only thing that I need to do to develop as a spiritual being.
- This is all I have to do for the benefit of Self, other, and the world.

Simple Candle Sadhana Exercise

1. Set your intention.
2. Choose your practice (candle exercise or another).
3. Pick regular time or set a specific period/interval to do the sadhana.
4. Make a commitment.

Daily Action

1. Set intention.
2. Light your Sadhana candle.
3. Blow out the candle immediately.
4. Do not think of the need to add more onto your Sadhana.
5. Doing no other practice than this begins a transformation process that will alter your life.
6. Trust in the process.

Religious sādhana, which both prevents an excess of worldliness and molds the mind and disposition (bhāva) into a form which develops the knowledge of dispassion and non-attachment. Sādhana is a means whereby bondage becomes liberation.

~N. Bhattacharyyan, historian

Sankalpa is a Sadhana practiced for a set period of time, a season, a moon cycle or any period that you desire. You may choose to do one simple Sadhana, such as the candle exercise, or you may create a daily Sadhana plan for each morning, for morning, noon, night or for each night during your Sankalpa. This is a set time to really focus on your intention and to connect to your Self. Daily self care and Ayurveda may be incorporated but the main practices are yogic in nature.

One immediate result of sadhana is the remembering! We begin to remember or AWAKEN to who we are. Consistently remembering and tapping into our higher Self is at the heart of all spiritual growth. One day we

32

will remember our spiritual essence in every single moment. That is the realized state, Samadhi. To paraphrase the great seeker Ram Das, as writes in *Be Here Now,* Sadhana literally becomes and is everything... and it is our hope that one day we will be that tapped in, that connected and that awake! That is the time where everything we do becomes Sadhana!

Start with a simple sadhana to build your confidence, discipline and commitment to your Self Care. Add another sadhana in addition to this one. Expand your sadhana time to include many practices that bring you joy. Start super small, remember the candle exercise.

Some examples are practicing yoga asana or other organic movement like Tai Chi, ecstatic dance, chanting, mala beads using a practice called Japa (inner mantra repetition usually 108 times), cleansing Ayurvedic actions like Abayangha (massaging the body with oil) or Nasya (oil with herbs for the sinuses) and kriya practices. When you blend practices together to create a mini practice sequence to be done for a period of time it is called a Sankalpa. Sankalpas are set to bring power and intention during special seasons of the Celtic calendar year or moon cycle.

Based on the number of days you do this, here is how it will affect your habits:

40 Days:

Practice every day for 40 days straight. This will break any negative habits that block you from the expansion possible through the kriya or mantra.

60 Days:

Practice every day for 60 days straight. This will establish a new habit in your conscious and subconscious minds based on the effect of the kriya or mantra. It will change you in a very deep way.

108 Days:

Practice every day for 108 days straight. This will confirm the new habit of consciousness created by the kriya or mantra. The positive benefits of the kriya get integrated permanently into your psyche.

1008 Days:

Practice every day for 1008 days straight. This will allow you to master the new habit of consciousness that the kriya or mantra has promised. No matter what the challenge, you can call on this new habit to serve you.

Remember, you are re-creating a new 'samakara', a new habit. It is an unconscious re-grooving of the mind, the glandular system and the nervous system; this is called neuroplasticity! We develop habits at a very young age. Some of them serve our Highest Good. Some of them do not. By doing a 40, 60, 108 or 1008 day special sadhana, you can rewire the brain and increase neuroplasticity. You can and will develop new, deeply ingrained habits that serve your Highest Good!

Sadhana is a Sanskrit word pronounced sah-dhah-nah with the inflection on the first syllable and the last 'h' being a soft breath out. According to Wikipedia it is literally 'a means of accomplishing something'. It is a spiritual practice that helps to transcend the ego mind. It includes a variety of disciplines that are followed in a ritualistic order to achieve various spiritual or ritual objectives.

The late B.K.S. Iyengar, the great guru of bringing yoga to the Western world, making it accessible to everyone was a beautiful teacher. In his English translation of and commentary to the Yoga Sutras of Patanjali[4] he is quoted defining sadhana in relation to abhyāsa, daily quiet time, and kriya, the yogic technique implemented to achieve the specific result.

As you can see, Sadhana is the foundation to your self care, your daily quiet time and the essence of your practice. I encourage you to create your

---

[4] B.K.S. Iyengar (1993: p. 22)

34

Sadhana and begin your practice immediately, if you have not already. This act alone will truly transform your life and if you take nothing else away from this text than acquiring and adhering to a daily Sadhana practice, then my work as an author is complete.

The Meaning Of OM

Oh Infinite Divine Mind, through my Beloved High Self;
Cleanse this unit of all negativity, both within and without,
so that is may be a perfect vessel for your presence.
~ Joe Vitale, The Zero Point

OM is a mystic syllable, considered the most sacred mantra in Hinduism and Tibetan Buddhism. It appears at the beginning and end of most Sanskrit recitations, prayers, and texts. OM is an ancient symbol that is found in ancient and medieval era manuscripts, temples, monasteries and spiritual retreats in Hinduism, Buddhism, and Jainism. The symbol has a spiritual meaning in all Indian dharmas, but the meaning and connotations of OM vary between the diverse schools within and across the various traditions.

In Hinduism, OM is one of the most important spiritual symbols (pratima). It refers to the soul, self within, Atman, and Brahman (ultimate reality, entirety of the universe, truth, divine, supreme spirit, cosmic principles, knowledge). The syllable is often found at the beginning and the end of chapters in the Vedas, the Upanishads, and other Hindu texts. It is a sacred spiritual incantation made before and during the recitation of spiritual texts, during private prayers, in ceremonies of burning (puja) and in rites of passages, sanskara, such as weddings, and sometimes during meditative and spiritual activities such as Yoga.

OM is all about sacred threes. Most faiths have trinities in their roots, such as the Father, The Son and the Holy Spirit in Christianity. In Hinduism, where OM was born, it is no different. Even though it's usually pronounced seamlessly so it rhymes with home, OM is made up of three syllables: A, U, and M, or, phonetically, 'aaah,' 'oooh,' and 'mmm' with a final vibration in the humming of the mmm leading into silence and the silent OM. Experts say these syllables can represent a slew of trios, including: the heavens, earth, and the underworld; the Hindu gods Brahma, Vishnu, and Shiva (aka creator god, sustainer god, and destroyer god); and the waking, dreaming, and dreamless states. The OM is 'to represent all of consciousness,' says Yogananda.

The sound appears to have first appeared in the Upanishads, a collection of sacred Eastern tests. The Mandukya Upanishad, which is entirely devoted to OM, begins with, "Om is the imperishable word. Om is the universe, and this is the exposition of om. The past, the present, and the future, all that was, all that is, all that will be is om. Likewise, all else that may exist beyond the bounds of time, that too is om."

OM is also considered the mother of the short, potent sounds that relate to each chakra, called bija or seed mantras. These sounds make up chants from simple to long, such as OM Shanti Shanti Shanti. It relates to the higher chakras, connecting us to our Divine Source.. Some say it's even among the sounds recorded in deep space on NASA's website, the sound of Earth itself.

My personal experience with the sound of OM was when I was first in the rainforest on the Big Island of Hawaii. We were in a treehouse sleeping in the middle of the jungle very close to the active volcano. I awoke to a sound so loud and so constant that I sat up in bed between my hubby and my daughter. I sat still listening to the soft rain, yet I heard the sound, the sound that is like a singing bowl, the sound of OM, the sound of Gaia, our Earth mother. I know it sounds crazy, and I agree, however I cannot deny what I heard, and it went on for hours. I eventually surrendered to not knowing where it was coming from and accepting that I was meant to stay warm and dry in my treehouse cabin. I however did take a remote USB from my camera bag and record the Hawaiian night, and I still have yet to replay it.

Some scholars say that the shape of the written om symbol embodies each of its syllables, the three is the Sanskrit letter for 'ahh, that same three with the mini S on it is 'oooh,' and the bindhi and half-moon at the top are the 'mmm.

OM is sacred simply because of its vibration; it is all about how we feel when we chant it.

Om unites us as a collective. When we sound OM together, we're aligning body, mind and spirit; we're aligning with one another. When we OM together we are aligning with the universe because it is the sound of the universe! This is something very real.

The final 'mmm' resonates in the skull and then fades into a hmmm then, the nothingness or silence in which we came from and where we will return, the true Essence that is always there. If we are still this is the sound of nothing, yet the sound of everything. This final sound, the sound of silence, is what many call the fourth syllable OM.

The Universe speaks in symbols and sound. Chanting OM creates a link with those who have practiced and walked this path before us. 'It's a sound that validates oneness and harmony. We chant it because yogis have for thousands of years. And when we chant it, we're connecting with those yogis in a ritual way, and drawing upon the support of the practices they've been doing for a long, long time, states Yogananda.

For one tiny sound, OM is deeply complex as it incorporates all the vowel sounds and reverberates in each go the energy centers in the body. Try these simple mouth adjustments just as you would shift a yoga posture to perfect it for your body. [5]

- For 'ahh', relax the jaw and throat. The sound rises from the belly, lips are parted softly, and the tongue doesn't touch the palate. This sound comes straight from the belly, just relax and feel it.
- In 'oooh', the lips gently come together in a circle as the sound moves from the belly into the heart.
- During 'mmm,' the lips gently close tongue floats in the mouth, and the lips come together to create a vibrating in the head. Often this syllable is twice as long as the others.
- Before stopping the 'mmm' close the throat by making a slight 'nngg' sound.
- Then the Silence, or the fourth syllable, follows while the allowing the sound to fade into Oneness.
- Feel the vibration in your body and skull. It will never go away, it is always there. This is the sound of OM, the Sound without a sound, the vibration of the Universe.
- You may learn to simply feel this sound in deep meditation.

- This sound is always in in the ears as a soft ringing when you get quite and go within you can hear it. Once you tune into that sound, it will always, always be there like a Light to guide us and center us. Peace, Love + Light.

---

[5] http://yoginirose.com/wp-content/uploads/2012/11/mantra-chanting-liner-notes.pdf

Prana and Chants for the Heart

Om Pranaya Namaha

Om Prana Pranaya Namaha

Om Prana Pranaya Namo Namo Namaha [6]

This chant honors the universal lifeforce energy of Prana. Namaha means to honor, recognize, and realize the inherent mystery of the one breath breathing us all. This chant is a natural breath exercise or pranayama, increasing the duration of your breath. Practice with this chant prana mudra, you can look up this mudra online. Taking the thumbs, cover the ring and pinkie fingers, extend the other two fingers with energy. You may also practice Prana Mudra with Abundance Mudra, bringing the arms up overhead in a V, also called Victory Mudra. This is a super powerful posture and mudra. Utlilizing this for chanting is extremely efficient and taps into something much greater than ourselves.

The following is a heart centered Sanskrit chant [7]:

Atma Hridaya

Hridaya Mayi

Hridaya Amritam

Amritam Anandam

---

[6] Shiva Rea, Prana Flow® a registered trademark of Prana Vinyasa
[7] Ramaswami, ADITYA HRUDAYAM- Sun in the Heart-from Ramayana-Srivatsa. See Ramaswami on YouTube for instructional/videos in Sanskrit

Translation of these chants:

My true nature is the heart (the heart is the self). The heart is my true nature (the heart is within me). I am the bliss of the heart (the nectar of the heart). The Heart that I am is the unending bliss of Oneness (this nectar is the bliss of the Self-Source). This is a chant to the heart from the heart.

The heart's true nature is to love for no reason at all. ~Dr. John Douillard

Chant this to feel yourself connecting into that true nature. Chanting in perfect rhythm is a natural pranayama! [8]Did you know Sanskrit is perfectly metered to be in a musical count? It is mathematic, and the language was not written, but discovered!

Next, we will look at the chant to study the Movements of Prana, honoring the directions and flow of Energy, the movements of the Universal Life Force. Here are the chants to honor the directions that energy moves.

Om Prana Swaha; Om Samana Swaha; Om Vyana Swaha; Om Apana Swaha; Om Udana Swaha! These are the five directions of energy movement, which we will study more in depth in future chapters.

When we speak of Prana with a capital 'P' we are speaking of the Universal Life Force. When we speak of prana with a small 'p' we are referring to our bodily human energy. Following are the beautiful, bhavana filled definitions from my master teacher Shiva Rea:

Prana : life is energy and breath, inhale fully

Vinyasa : life is cycles of waves, learn to surf

---

[8] T.K.V. Desikachar and Kaustab Desikachar for the teachings of integrating chanting as pranayama

Yoga : life is a unified field, relax into oneness

Parinama : life is change, be open

Spanda : life is vibrating consciousness, awaken

Shakti : life is creative energy, celebrate your essence

Unmesa : life contracts, have no fear

Nimesa : life expands, transform limitations

Tala : life is rhythm, find your pulse

Prasara : life is flow, ride the wave

Rasa : Life is full of juice, savor each moment

Prema : Life is infinite love, burst the dam swim

Sukha : Life is inherent happiness, embody joy without external needs

Sangha : life is community, participate fully

Mandala : life is wholeness, be and see 360 degrees

Bindu : life returns and emerges from the conscious seed, bow to the source

Nataraj : life is an eternal dance, om namah shivaya

Bandhas, Yogic Energy Locks

Root introduction to the bandhas, these are the interior body locks or anatomical internal diaphragms used for holding energy and supporting the

41

energy and body breathing practices and yoga postures. There are three bandhas; Mula Bandha, Uddiyana Bandha and Jhalandara Bandha. Combining all three with breathing exercise in conjunction takes dedicated practice. When all three are combined it is called the Master Bandha, 'Maha Bandha' or Great Lock. Each bandha is in itself an energetic lock, or a gateway, like in a channel of water. It is used for supporting and/or closing off of parts of the interior body. These locks are used in various breathing, or pranayama, practices and used in postures, or asanas, to tone, cleanse and energize the interior body and organs.

Mula Bandha

Root lock is the first of three interior body locks used in asana and pranayama practice to control the flow of energy, and it is the most vital to master. To activate mula bandha, exhale and engage the pelvic floor, drawing in and upwards towards your navel. If you don't know how to access the pelvic floor, think of it as the space between the pubic bone and the tailbone, the perineum. You feel it when you cut off the flow of urine or in women when you do a kegel exercise, or in men when you step into a pool of cold water. Initially you may need to contract and hold the muscles around the anus and genitals, but that is not idea. What you want is to isolate and draw up the perineum, which is the triangle of muscle and flesh between the anus and genitals. Do not hold your breath. Engaging mula bandha, root lock, is kind of like an internal kiss, a pucker, yet so subtle. While doing yoga it is essential to your practice and is used for support in almost all postures. It can give the poses extra lift and power. This is especially useful when jumping, or doing standing postures, arm balances or inversions.

Pronunciation: Moo-la Ban-d-huh (the last h is a soft exhale not a hard h). Alternate Spellings: Moola Bandha.

42

Uddiyana Bandha

Upper Abdominal lock is the second of the three interior body locks used in asana and pranayama practice to control the flow of energy. Uddiyana bandha can be practiced alone or most often in conjunction with mula bandha. To engage this bandha, sit in a comfortable cross legged position. Exhale your breath all the way, pushing the diaphragm belly button to spine. Take a false inhale drawing the abdomen in and up lifting the ribs, as if inhaling, without taking in any breath. Push the bellybutton in and up with the diaphraghm. To release, soften the abdomen and inhale slowly. Uddiyana bandha tones, massages and cleanses the abdominal organs. If you are familiar with mula bandha, you will see that the drawing up of the pelvic floor naturally leads into the drawing up of the abdomen. This is how the bandhas work together.

Pronunciation: Oo-di-yana Ban-d-huh

Jhalandara Bandha

Throat lock is the third of the three primary interior body locks used in asana and pranayama practice to control the flow of energy. Jhalandara bandha can be practiced alone or in conjunction with mula bandha and uddiyana bandha. To engage this bandha, sit in a comfortable seated position. Inhale so the lungs are completely full, pause at the top of the breath, the kumbhaka, and then hold the breath in. Lift the heart center and lock the chin to chest drawing the chin back and down so that the back of the neck does not round. Hold as long as is comfortable and then bring the chin level with the horizon to open the throat, slowly release the breath and come back to your normal breath. To practice in conjunction with the other two bandhas, first draw the pelvic floor upwards, engaging Mula Bandha. This leads to the abdomen drawing in and up under the ribcage , lift the ribcage and hold Uddiyana Bandha. Finally, drops to the chin to the chest and draw the throat back into Jhalandara Bandha. When practiced together, the three locks are known as Maha Bandha, the great lock, as stated.

Pronunciation: Jal-an-daura Ban-d-huh

Ujjayi Victorious Breath

Deep Three-part Yogic Breathing is known as Ujjayi. It is derived from the Sanskrit root 'ji' with the prefix 'ud added to it. So the combined root is 'ujji' which means 'to be victorious', thus it is know as the Breath of Victory or Victorious Breath. It is the vital pranayama to a healthy Vinyasa practice and is the most widely practiced breath during yoga asana (yogasana) or yoga class. [9]

Ujjayi means 'one who is victorious' and Ujjayi breath would mean 'the victorious breath'.

Because of the various benefits it provides Ujjayi is recommended as the breathing technique to be used during any of the physical yoga practices such as asana or pranayama that require you to breathe deeper than your natural breath. While practicing Sun Salutations, or the proper name of Surya Namaskar, it is recommended that each movement be made slowly and totally in sync with the appropriate deep inhalation or exhalation. Since the breathing is slow and deep, Ujjayi is recommended as one breath per movement in the flow of Vinyasa, then using three to five breaths when in standing, warrior and seated poses. Similarly, while practicing pranayama techniques involving deep breathing, like the alternate nostril breathing, called Nadi Shodhana, it is recommended to use the ujjayi breath technique.

---

[9] http://yogawithsubhash.com/2010/08/07/ujjayi-victorious-breath/

Technique for Ujjayi

Ujjayi is practiced while breathing through the nose and narrowing the throat by partially closing the epiglottis, the piece of cartilage at the top of your larynx. This produces a slight hissing sound (it may also be compared to a Darth Vader breath or the sound of the ocean). This sound is a result of friction of the incoming or outgoing air at the base of the throat and not from friction in the nostrils. Let that sound become your guide, like listening to the sound in a seashell. As you inhale and exhale, and make that breath as even and smooth as you can, without any catches or wavering and without any change in pitch. The sound should be soft and gentle and only you should be able to hear its sound, maybe the person next to you, but not someone across the room. Listening to your Ujjayi pranayama will give you greater sensitivity and control over the nuances of your breath.

At first, you may wonder exactly how to manipulate this epiglottal valve at the root of your throat to make that ocean breath sound.

Here are a few helpful techniques which can help you learn this vital pranayama:

- Just sigh. Notice the slight constriction in your throat that occurs. That's the area you need to control when you're practicing Ujjayi.

- Open your mouth and inhale softly, noticing where the breath touches your throat. For most people, that will be deep down at the base and back of the throat. Again, that's the spot you need to constrict slightly to practice Ujjayi. After you've zeroed in on this area, close your mouth and inhale, letting the breath touch your throat there. Once you can inhale in this way, practice exhaling with the same constriction of the epiglottis.

- Hold your hand up to your mouth and exhale as if trying to fog a mirror. Inhale the same way.

- Notice how you constrict the back of the throat to create the fog effect. Now close your mouth and do the same exhale as if fogging up a mirror while breathing out through the nose.
- Touch the tongue to the back of the teeth where they meet the top gums, loosen the jaw and unclench the teeth while keeping the lips closed. This creates an open space at the back of the throat for the air to swirl around.

Practice this breath often, especially during your asana. Go ahead and try it now!

Benefits of Ujjayi

Ujjayi is a calming, meditative breath. It increases Prana, as it has a heating effect on the body. Ujjayi in Vinyasa is super important to mindfully connect the breath to the practice and move energy. It is a breath also commonly used in yoga therapy, as when practiced mindfully it helps to soothe the nervous system and calm the mind. It has a deeply relaxing effect on the mind. It is said to help with insomnia and may be practiced in Savasana, final relaxation, and also just before sleep. The basic breath is practiced without breath retention and bandhas. When practiced this way it is said to slow down the heart rate and may be useful for people with high blood pressure. Ujjayi breathing is also stated to help alleviate fluid retention. Ujjayi breathing is referenced in Ayurveda, the sister science of yoga, the science of medicine. It is said that when practiced regularly and intentionally it may have great potential to balance and remove disorders of the Dhatu.

The Dhatu are the seven constituents of the body:

- o   Blood
- o   Bone
- o   Marrow
- o   Fat

- o Semen
- o Skin
- o Flesh

Practicing Ujjayi is a natural breathing technique that creates a habit to breathe deeper than your normal deep breath. When you use Ujjayi during asana practice to synchronize movement with the deeper breath, as in Vinyasa Yoga, it brings great sense of awareness of the effect of the pose, as well as helps to set the intention for your practice.

Simple and Effective Breathing Techniques

Many people find the active lifestyle that they lead causes tension and irritability. Lack of sleep, multi-tasking and eating fast foods is a contributor to building up stress in our bodies. When daily activities begin to take a toll, the emotions begin to become affected. Reactions may not be well thought out; people become much less pro active.

By taking a few simple breaths these symptoms and stressors will dissipate. One easy and attainable breathing technique to use is called 3 Part Breath. To access this breath, simply find easy seated position. Lift the heart and crown high; create space between the vertebrae. Relax the chin so its level with the earth. Sink back into the tailbone; release the lower back. Now, begin to focus on the sound of the breath. Soften the any areas that are holding tension, letting that drain into the earth. Breathe through the belly, through the chest, to the crown of the head. Slowly release, reversing the flow through the nose, through the throat, the chest and begin to squeeze out through the belly, coming to no breath. If comfortable, pause without breath. Utilizing the pelvic floor muscles, feel the breath again rise inhaling through the nose, the belly, the chest and pause at the top of the breath. Then slowly release. Continue this pattern as long as is enjoyable, listening to the sound of breath and letting go.

Three part breath can be practiced during any activity, even while driving. As few as three breaths can make a huge difference. As this breath becomes more natural, more awareness will begin to come into view. This will enlighten and call attention to when the breath is retained, and then can be released. Begin to realize that mind, body, and spirit are all interconnected!

Moon Goddess Practices

This is my personal story of my Chandra Sankalpa, Moon practice, followed by a Yin, Reflective Guided Meditation.

I am a moon baby, a moon goddess. I love gazing at the moon. To me it is a sacred practice, and one that has been held for eons. It harmonizes one's mind and heart with the lunar cycle, which is so important for our circadian rhythms. Moon gazing also serves as instantly creating a deep and reflective meditative space. It helps to reset our own natural rhythm of sleep and waking, and is especially good for healing insomnia. It helps us to reset and for me I feel so totally recharged! I also like setting all my crystals and stones out in the full moon for a lovely moon recharge. I use my stones throughout the month, and that reset really brings the frequency back up! Paying attention to the journey from new to full and full to new is a practice, and can be a Sadhana, if you set your intention as such. Cultivation of this lunar bhavana, or reverence, is to awaken and be fully in tune with the elements of the Cosmos, bringing us into greater alignment with who we really are as humans.

Utilizing pranayama focused on the lunar breath is a shift toward being receptive. We utilize the lunar power to find deep relaxation, the watery lunar fluidity of grace and we also tap back into ourselves. There is a yogic metaphor for this; it is called 'the nectar of the moon'. It refers to this Divine lunar flow. You can develop a lunar practice by paying close attention to the

48

moon cycle, I even use an app to track the sunrise and sunset and the cycles of the moon. It is surprising how quickly we get caught up in daily life! Using tools like a gentle phone reminder, your crystals, and many more will help you to not only integrate, but to apply this bhavana, Divine feeling, and use this knowledge as a self healing practice.

I especially like to practice yoga at full moon and new moon. My teachings are so dynamic, downloaded straight from Source in the flow. This is a time when I write and receive Divine serendipity with so many countless people and opportunities. I notice the energy rising as the full moon draws near, and my creative juices begin to flow! Many full moons I have manifested projects, ideas, money and material things, as well as some amazing teaching sequences, which I have recorded and written. I encourage you to begin a lunar practice of your own.

For years I was fearful to do a drop-back from Tadasana (mountain pose) to Urdhva Dhanurasana (Wheel Pose). I began a Sankalpa that I plan to keep for the rest of my life. Many moons! I have for many years held respect for yogis who can stand in Tadasana, Mountain pose, and drop back to Wheel pose with such bravery and seeming ease. So, many years ago, to continually challenge myself and face my fear (fear is False Evidence Appearing Real) I committed to begin a full moon practice of learning to drop back. At first I really had to sit with it to even get brave enough to attempt it. You see, it is not the strength that is lacking, I could do Wheel from the ground up, and of course I could stand in Mountain pose. However, when you simply fall backwards onto the earth without looking and landing on your hands it seemed daunting, to say the least.

So I began to drop back uphill onto the hillside out back by the waterfall, so the fall was not so far. Then I began to drop back onto less of a hill. (Don't drop back onto a folding lawn chair, not a good idea). Every full moon I would go outside, gaze at the moon in gratitude, gathering beauty and letting go. Then I would just do it.

Surprisingly it really is not that far back! The next thing I began to notice was that my arms were much stronger than I thought, and as long as my elbows did not bend too much I would not fall out!

Remember, this sadhana is a once a month practice, so it has taken a long time to see documentable progress. But in yoga slow and steady wins the race!

Then, I began to try to pop back up into Tadasana from Wheel sometimes I would fall onto the ground and get leaves in my hair, sometimes wet rainy grass on my jammies, or even ice and snow and sometimes I would land and not really prep well to come back up and fall into Bridge or flat on the Earth. Yet the moon, she calls!! And ohhh... those dreamy summer full moonlit nights! I stand with the back of my heart center to the moon, just receiving, recharging, with heart and arms wide open, mmm...

Many times I did this practice right before bed because I would all of a sudden remember, 'Oh my!!! It's the full moon and I haven't done my backbend!!!' So I run out full monty and just do it!!! In December of 2017 right before finishing this book, I even forgot to do my sankalpa on a night that it was so cold in Texas. I did it anyway ...when it was 11 degrees out, and guess what? I was naked!!! That LITERALLY was the world's fastest drop back!!!

It was exhilarating to say the least! My hubby thinks I am a bit crazy, and you may too. Yet in some way aren't we all?

My point in sharing this is to say that sometimes when you go for it you may land in horse poop, but GET UP and keep doing your practice. Daily tiny bits of progress don't seem like a lot, but when jump 4 years ahead and see yourself looking back 52 moons.... where can you see yourself? Just think and envision that person you are stepping into! How exciting!

One of the most important ways to develop abundance is to create Self time to connect to Source. This daily time consists of spiritual and physical practices that enhance your own energy and help you to connect to something Greater than yourself. This is called a Sadhana. As the Great Ram Dass stated, everything is Sadhana. This means living in total flow with Oneness, connection to Divine Goddess, or however you see that connection.

Lunar Breath, New Moon to Full

Moon Cycle Creative Visualization Breath[10] is a pranayama for the moon cycle, reflecting the cycles within our own bodies, as we reflect on the Celestial lunar body of the moon.

As you are gazing at the actual moon, or a visualized moon or a photo of the moon, draw the inhale from that reflective light down through the crown of the head through the backs of the eyes, just like honey or nectar, moving through the creases of the brain, it is a mystical experience. The Inhale is the cooling breath associated with the lunar nectar, the regenerative energy of the moon. The journey on the inhale follows the moon cycle from the new moon, starting at the crown of the head, to the full moon, at the heart. There are four parts to the breath. Puraka - Inhalation, Rechaka - Exhalation, Kumbhaka - Retention of the breath. [11] There is the greatest concentration of the lunar energy at the very tip top of the inhale, and pause, the is the kumbhaka. Then as you exhale, it is the journey from the full moon to the new moon, back up from the heart to the crown of the head. This waning energy gives us the opportunity for us to let go with every exhale. Open your heart by using the gaze out from your heart, as if your heart had eyes, seeing and feeling the world through your heart. This is your hridaya drishti, heart gaze.

---

[10] Tantric meditation of Ucchara - translated by Chris Tompkins for Shiva Rea
[11] https://www.yogaindailylife.org/system/en/exercise-levels/the-full-yoga-breath

With a long spine, feel your inhale (drawing down the moon) by visualizing a stream of lunar nectar flowing from the lotus at the crown of the head. As you're gazing at the moon, draw your inhale from the crown to the heart as the expression of increasing light. From the crown of the head to the heart is the journey from the new moon to the full moon, a time to nourish whatever has been creating inside you. Picture the phases of the moon as you breathe.

- Begin by inhaling the lunar nectar from the crown of the head, slowly with Ujjayi breathing, down into the heart center. (new moon)
- Follow this nectar from the crown of the head (new moon) to your third eye center (quarter moon).
- Follow the lunar energy from the third eye center to the palate of the mouth (half moon).
- Bring this energy from the soft palate of the mouth to your throat center (3/4 waxing moon).
- Feel the lunar energy gather as you bring it from your throat center through to your heart center (full moon).
- You can pause in kumbhaka (at the tip top of the inhale).
- You may also include a lunar mantra – OM hrim Lakshmi-ya Namaha (or any other mantras that resonate with you). This is where the Sun, moon and fire of the heart align with the crown of the head.
- As you exhale, slowly release the breath passing back out up from the center of your heart, through the throat, up through the soft palate at the top of the mouth, through the third eye center and up and into the Universe through the crown of the head, as if exhaling the waning moon.
- Complete one, two or three working up to 108 rounds.
- Practice regularly; it is always especially nice to practice outdoors.
- Complete the process by resting in natural meditation

- Find dedication to something greater.
- Close your practice with gratitude and apppreciaton.

Solar Breath Meditation

This is a Solar, yang prana building energy practice for summer Solstice, or daily for honoring the sunrise and/or sunset. The solar breath cycle is based upon Tantric meditation. It is envisioned as the union of the sun (surya) and the moon (chandra) with the life force of Prana, with the fire within the heart. Each breath can also be visualized as the full cycle of the sun or the full cycle of the moon. Bringing awareness to on both the in-breath and out-breath is a vital part of this cycle.

As you're gazing upon the sun, or a depiction of the sun, or even a candle, we actually begin to physically and energetically draw the solar life force, or prana, right into our heart. We do this through our breath. As you inhale, feel that solar radiance drawing into your body through the following meditation, using the seasonal cycles as a reference.

- Inhale bringing in the solar energy from the Universe into crown of the head (Summer solstice)
- Follow the solar energy to your third eye (Beltane)
- Third eye center to the palate of the mouth (Equinox, both spring and fall)
- From the palate of the mouth to your throat center (Samhain, All Saints Day)
- Throat center through to your heart center (Winter solstice).
- Bow your chin towards your heart and pause in kumbhaka (inhale retention without straining) and feel the space outside of time. Offer prayers and mantras within that space as offerings to the inner heart fire.

- Practice Om, bija mantras, the solar mantra Om Hum Suraye Namaha, the Gayatri Mantra
- Practice meditation on solar Archetypes such as Shiva, Durga, Hanuman, Ram.
- As you exhale, feel the solar breath return from the heart center back to the crown. Continue to breathe the light of the sun through the circulation of your breath with the option of meditating with feeling, bhavana, and mantra. You can enjoy for several rounds then rest in meditation or utilize a mantra as you repeat it internally, japa.
- Complete the process by resting in natural meditation by closing your practice and dedication.

Metta; Truth, Maintaining the Spiritual Path

Dissolve all limiting beliefs! Divinity will appear! At any moment you are either experiencing a memory or an inspiration.

~ Joe Vitale, The Zero Point

Metta is the practice of living in self truth (satya), self love and honesty. These practices are taught in the yamas and niyamas. Practicing metta in our every day actions helps us to remain on a pure path to enlightenment. Metta is about loving one self, as no one else can ever love you more then you love yourself. The following are three primary qualities of living in a path of Self love and some helpful tips to stay the path.

Truth is essential for maintenance of your Path. Be honest with yourself. Be honest with others. Be honest with your environment and Mother Earth; treat her gently and with great love and reverence.

Have Wisdom and practice strong boundries and renunciation of anything that steers you from your True Self. Give up whatever separates you from your spiritual nature. Give up the addiction to self-identity, our hats/roles. This is also referred to as the ego. The ego is very difficult to find, unless you intentionally spend quiet time with Spirit. Focus on right speech, right thoughts and right emotions. Give up addictive behaviors and habits. Ask for help when needed. Pray and meditate daily.

Generosity, helps us get out of ourselves. Also, giving to your own self with Daily Self care and time to create, play and relax. Give back to the community and to others. Our true spiritual nature is to be free! Accept yourself as you are... unconditionally. You are a beautiful, powerful, amazing child of Creator!

Know your spiritual Self's five ENEMIES

- Craving (for sensual pleasure)

- Aversion (ill-will/hatred)

- Sluggishness (laziness)

- Agitation (restlessness)

- Doubt (about your higher Self or your true path)

Know your spiritual Self's five FRIENDS

- Faith (devotion to your spiritual path)

- Effort (determination and hard work)

- Awareness (your mindfulness)

- Concentration (your meditation anchor)

- Wisdom (experience balance of mind)

Begin acting 'as if' you are your spiritual Self! Believe, have faith in your ability to change and create the life of your dreams! You are the creator of infinite abundance in your life! Abundance is always there, it is the Universal Law! Our work is to remove the unconscious blockages with our practices and we will become completely aligned with our highest Source.

Fake it, until you make it

~ Mary Kay Ash, American Female Entrepreneur

Kundalini Awakening, Ida and Pingala

Prana is life force. It is made to flow in both sides of the body equally. These sides of the energetic body are referred to Ida and Pingala. This energetic flow shifts back and forth from Ida to Pingala in periods of approximately ninety minutes during most of the day. The central channel of energy is called the Shushuma channel. It lies just about 3 centimeters in front of the spine and cannot be physically manipulated, unlike Ida and Pingala. Shushuma is awakened when Ida and Pingala are equally balanced and stimulated. This is sometimes referred to as a Kundalini awakening, or the rising of the dormant coiled snake. Kundalini awakening is the reaction of awakened pranic energy moving up the shushuma channel of energy and is something that most humans fail to tap into, unless they have a conscious practice of yoga. [12]

Hatha Yoga balances Ida and Pingala. The entire purpose of Hatha Yoga is the balancing of the energies of Ida and Pingala. Ida is lunar, Pingala is solar. HA means sun and THA means moon. The sun is the active energy of Pingala. The moon is the passive energy of Ida. The union of these two energies is called Yoga, which means union or wholeness, or to yoke.

---

[12] http://www.swamij.com/kundalini-awakening-2.htm

Pingala runs along the right side of the shushuma channel, Ida runs along the left side of the central channel, for descriptive purposes. This is energy, and therefore this is metaphorically speaking. All energy is affected by the chakra system, which we will discuss in great detail in later chapters.

In the ancient text, the Hatha Yoga Pradipika, the first of the four chapters deals, in large part, with postures. However, the second chapter deals squarely with the issue of Kundalini Awakening, followed by chapters on advancing to Raja Yoga. Yoga Sutras 2.52 is specifically talking about pranayama, Sutra 2.52: tata kshiyate prakasha avaranam. Loosely translated as when pranayama is done correctly the darkness of the human afflictions are removed and the brighteness of our true nature is revealed.

The Hatha postures and breathing practices all help to balance Ida and Pingala, where they are both flowing freely. The breath practices of three part breathing and Two-to-One Ratio Breathing are especially helpful. The vigorous breathing practice of Kapalabhati, breath of fire can help to break the pattern of being stuck in Ida or Pingala. I practice Kapalabhati regularly in the morning to move the energy from being stuck in one nostril when I awaken, and after 108 rounds the energy always shifts and begins to regulate. This feels amazing to get the prana flowing in the morning right upon awakening!

Balancing Ida and Pingala also balances the sympathetic and parasympathetic branches of the autonomic nervous system. This reduces the elevated flight or fight response. The single act of balancing the breath is a primary aid in reducing physical stress. Also, these practices set the stage for a strong spiritual practice and Kundalini Awakening.

The first step in causing Ida and Pingala to flow evenly to help create an environment where Kundalini Awakening is possible is balancing the flow of energy. This means that equal amounts of Prana are flowing in the left and right sides. It is most readily evidenced by the breath flowing evenly in the two nostrils.

In our culture, we may speak of feeling off-balance or getting balanced. We speak of wanting to be centered. The goal of this step of the Kundalini Awakening process is to balance and center the energy. This affects not only the subtle bodies, but is also experienced in the physical body and all the layers, or the koshas, of the body. These practices bring wonderful health benefits by positively regulating the autonomic nervous system.

In Ayurveda it is studied that there is a natural transition between Ida and Pingala from time to time during the day. For those with very healthy bodies and minds, this shift happens approximately every 90 minutes. For others, the shift may not follow so naturally, or energy may be more or less stuck in either Ida or Pingala for much longer periods of time during the 24 hours of the day.

It is in these moments of natural transition that the mind is in a natural calm, centered, or balanced state. It is as if there is a mini free meditation available many times a day, if only we pay attention to our bodies. There is a sense of deep inner peace, as if the mind wants to do nothing but to simply just be. For most of us, unaware of this transition, we force ourselves to keep going in our world during these moments. It is possible we write these moments off to thinking we are just sleepy. Now that you are aware of this natural shifting, this awareness provides a time to take just a minute for yourself every day, even a few time during the day to enjoy the inner stillness. It is literally as if nature is giving us a super simple way to just check in.

The union or balancing of Ida and Pingala is like a marriage, called Sandhya. It is the wedding of surya and Chandra, solar and lunar, day and night. This is a time of great meditative joy. In this union the mind and the breath are joined.

The balancing of Ida and Pingala is manipulated by asana, pranayama and intention causing Prana to flow evenly. This union of sun and moon is the real beginning of true joy in meditation. All of the other practices to this point are simply setting the stage to attain this peace of mind. This state is where the real practice of meditation begins. Meditation is truly joyful, not a discipline. We do the discipline and the reward is true Joy! [13]

Within the practice of yoga, pranayama and meditation, the practitioner naturally desires to be able to balance these two energies by direct control. Many different breathing practices are done to balance Ida and Pingala, allowing them to flow evenly. These practices are extremely useful and build a solid foundation.

The ability to regulate the balance of breath by focusing the mind on the flow in the nostrils, though a simple practice, is one of the most profound parts of the inner journey. To do this, simply notice with your mind which nostril is flowing more and which is flowing less freely. By focusing strong attention on the closed or less open nostril, it will gradually open, and bring an increased feeling of calm. This may take some months to accomplish, or it may come sooner, but this will definitely come with practice.

Another way to notice the active nostril flow is to place the back of the hand under the nose and exhale. Notice which side creates more air flow, then do this test again after your practice of yoga or pranayama or Reiki. This flow may balance out or change to the other side. There is no goal or outcome here, simply just observe.

---

[13] http://www.mind-and-body-yoga.com/kundalini-meditation.html

So-Hum Mantra

The So-Hum Mantra is one of the simplest mantras to remember because it is based on the sound that the breath naturally makes. As you breathe there are primarily two sounds, Sooooooo with inhalation, and Hummmmmm with exhalation. Conscious use of the so-hum mantra is a tremendous aid in balancing Ida and Pingala. The So-Hum Mantra can be a useful tool for difficult asana, stressful days and tapping into the place in meditation where the mind gets quiet.[14]

In our Western culture during the day most people are busy. It is useful to know about the difference between Ida and Pingala dominance in relation to when to plan activities.

When the right nostril is open is when Pingala is dominant, this is a good time to do more active projects, as the solar energy is naturally flowing. When the left nostril is open Ida is predominantly active. Ida operates the lunar side of our nature and therefore during these times it is appropriate do more introspection and creative projects.

In relation to digestion and diet, ideally, solid foods are taken when Pingala is more active. This is when the right nostril is open aiding in digestion. Pingala is more dominant in midday; therefore noon-ish is usually the best time to take the major meal of the day, meaning when the sun is highest eat your biggest meal. Ideally, liquids are taken when Ida is more prevalent. This is when the left nostril is open. Of course, remain flexible about these principles, as it is simply energy.

We are all energetic beings living in this precarious shell for 100 or so years! The more aware we are of this fact, the more opportunity Spirit gives

---

[14] http://www.swamij.com/cd-sabbatical.htm

us to tap in. Using these tools can help bring you into a greater state of awareness of who you are and why you are here.

Kundalini Meditation Sa Ta Na Ma

This meditation is a simple meditation and one of the first I teach my students that study the deeper path of yoga. It is also very good for beginners in meditation because it offer two focal points to keep your mind from wandering. The first tool is the mantra and the other is the finger touch points.The Mantra being used is Sa Ta Na Ma. The meaning of this Mantra is very simple.

Sa means Birth, it represents the beginning (of all things including the meditation and your journey, either spiritual, physical or mental), it also represents infinity.

Ta represents Life, both your own and all life on this planet, as well as the interconnection to the Cosmos.

Na represents Death or the end of something (your stress for example or negative thoughts, or the end of a cycle) It is about totality. Because death is the sum of everything it gives completion a view of the whole of something.

Ma represents rebirth or resurrection. When we thing of this we can also relate this to a change in ourselves, our surroundings or birthing a creative project or idea coming into manifestation.

While sitting in Sukasana, simple seated yoga posture, chant the above mantra while simultaneously focusing your attention on the finger touch points. Sit with your palms up and resting on your knees touch your thumb to the corresponding finger to the mantra.

- Sa: touch to the index finger to the thumb.
- Ta: touch the middle finger to the thumb.

61

- Na: touch the ring finger to the thumb.
- Ma: touch the pinky finger to the thumb.

You can practice slow or fast, depending on how fast your mind is going that day. As yo settle into your mantra, you will naturally begin to slow down. To get the most out of your meditation practice you must practice it every day for at least three weeks. The recommended practice for this meditation is one time in the early morning for about 3 minutes and again in the evening for 3 minutes. Working yourself up to five then ten minutes is ideal. After practicing regularly for just a week or so you will begin to notice subtle changes in yourself. You may seem more relaxed, become much slower to anger and less stressed.

Recommended Meditation Posture

Choosing a preferred meditation posture to use for meditation is important to learn. When we practice meditation we must to have somewhere comfortable and relaxing to sit and it is very important to have good posture, but also be relaxed. The most important feature of the posture is to keep our spine straight. To help us do this, sit on a cushion making sure that the back of the cushion is slightly higher than the front. This will incline the pelvis slightly forward. It is not necessary at first to sit in simple seated, but it is a good idea to become accustomed to sitting in Lotus pose or Half Lotus as we develop our practice. If we cannot hold this posture, we should sit in one which is as close to this as possible while remaining comfortable.

Lotus posture is the ideal posture for advanced meditation practices. Following are the primary features to the Lotus posture. Lotus is called Padmasana in Sanskrit, sometimes called Vairochana.

To practice Lotus Posture:

The legs are crossed under you. Lift one ankle and place it on your opposite thigh. Ensure that the ankle bone is fully over the femur to prevent ankle from sickling or supinating, and that both sides of the ankle remain even. This is half lotus or Ardha Padmasaa. For full lotus both ankles are be over each thigh. Lotus helps to reduce thoughts and also detach from feelings and emotions. The flower blooms out of the muddy water, unscathed. It is only from being in the mud that we blossom into our fullest potential and beauty!

Using a mudra is like yoga for the hands. The lotus mudra in conjunction with the lotus posture is especially beautiful. To do the lotus mudra simply place the base of the palms together and bring the fingers to face upward. Place the pinkies and the thumbs together and spread out the other three fingers with energy to form a flower. Try bringing the lotus in front of first your heart chakra, sitting with that for several breaths up to several minutes. Then move the mudra to above the crown chakra, then in front of your third eye and finally the throat chakra before moving back to the heart. Expore what comes up.

Meditation mudra is another great mudra for using in lotus. It is performed with palms upwards and cupped, right hand placed inside the left hand. The the tips of the thumbs are slightly raised and gently touching, making a small, soft oval. The hands are held about four fingers width below the navel, wrists may be resting on the legs. This helps us to develop good concentration.

In any seated posture the back is straight but do not make the muscles in your back tense. This helps to develop and maintain a clear mind, and it allows the subtle energy of our body's to flow freely.

The mouth and lips are closed and relaxed, not tense. The way to soften the breath and the jaw is to use the yogic tongue position. The tip of the tongue should touch the back of the upper teeth and gums, jaw soft. This prevents excessive salivation, as well as preventing your mouth from becoming too dry. It also aids greatly in Ujayii breathing by creating a space in the back of the throat for the air to swirl around. Listen to the sound of the breath like the sound of the ocean or if you were listening to a large sea shell.

The head is tipped ever so slightly forward with the chin tucked in, a slight throat lock, Jalandhara Bandha. The drishdi is the focal point for the eyes. In this pose focus down at a single spot on the Earth in front of you. This helps calm mental energy. Align the crown chakra directly above the root chakra, creating a natural flow in the central channel, shushuma. It is ideal to maintain this line of prana, in an upward flow, without creating tension or too much distraction.

The eyes are relaxed and slightly open with the gaze downward and a soft gaze. With a soft and relaxed gaze we keep your attention active while the same time staying mentally relaxed, almost as if looking into a soft focal point and all else becomes cloudy in the peripheral vision.

The shoulders are level and the elbows are relaxed, but slightly away from the sides to allow the lungs to expand fully.When you practice regularly these become simple and second nature. We all start somewhere. The idea is to simply begin. Remember, this is just yoga!

Three Part Breathing, Dirga Pranayama

Three Part breath is pronounced Dirga Swasam Pranayama (DEER-gah swha-SAHM prah-nah-YAH-mah) in Sanskrit. The full name comes from two Sanskrit words. Dirga (also spelled Deerga) has several meanings, including, slow, deep, long and complete. Swasam refers to the breath. Therefore, this practice is sometimes also referred to as Complete Breath. It is also often simply called Dirga Pranayama. This is often the first breathing technique taught to new yoga practitioners. The three parts are the belly, diaphragm, and chest. During Three Part Breath, you first completely fill your lungs with air, as though you are breathing into your belly, ribcage, and upper chest. Then you exhale completely, reversing the flow.

64

Three part breathing is one of my favorite go to breath practice to do and to teach. It focuses the attention on the present moment and it calms and grounds the mind. Many students come to their mat ungrounded from the day, and so starting proactively with a strong three part breathing pranayama is a gateway to maintaining a focus of calm and peace for the remainder of the practice.

This pranayama exercise is often done while seated in a comfortable, cross-legged position, but it is also nice to do while lying on the back, particularly at the end of your practice. When you are lying down, you can really feel the breath moving through your body as it makes contact with the Earth.

How to practice Three Part Breath

Sitting in easy Seated, Sukasana or Lotus, relax the face and the body. Activate root lock. Begin by observing the natural inhalation and exhalation of your breath without changing or shaping anything. If you find yourself distracted by the thoughts in your mind, try not to engage in the thoughts. Just notice them like a big puffy white cloud on a blue sky day, and then let them go, bringing your attention back to the inhales and the exhales, the blue sky.

Begin to inhale deeply through the nose, using your Ujayii breathing. On each inhale, fill the belly up with your breath. Expand the chest and pull ribs up with air like a lifting up the handle on a bucket. You have the option to use throat lock here at the top of the breath. Pause. Hold throat lock, if engaged.

On the exhale, using Udyhana Bandha press the belly button in and up towards the spine squeezing out all the air. Make sure you are breathing out through your nose. Draw the navel back and up towards your spine making sure that the lungs are totally empty of all residual tidal volume of air.

Hold all three locks as long as you are able, Maha Bandha the Great Bandha. To inhale, simply unlock the throat slowly and the air will begin to seep in. On the next inhale, fill the belly up with air all the way to the top of the breath. When the belly is full, draw in a little more breath and let that air expand into the rib cage causing the ribs to widen apart. On the exhale, let the air go first from the rib cage, letting the ribs slide closer together, and them from the belly, drawing the navel back towards the spine.

Repeat this deep breathing into the belly and rib cage for about five breaths. On the next inhale, fill the belly and rib cage up with air then draw in just a little more air and let it fill the upper chest, all the way up to the collarbone, causing the area around the heart center, expand and rise. On the exhale, let the breath go first from the upper chest, allowing the heart center sink back down, then from the rib cage, letting the ribs slide closer together.

Lastly, let the air out starting from the belly, drawing the navel back and up towards the spine. Continue at your own pace, eventually coming to let the three parts of the breath happen smoothly, working to seamlessly move between inhales and exhales for about 3 to 5 minutes.

Yogic breathing, or pranayama, is an important component in developing your practice and is one of the eight limbs of yoga. According to the ancient text, the Yoga Sutras, compiled by the sage Patanjali in 150 BCE, pranayama is the fourth of the classical Eight Limbs, or Petals, of Yoga. Practicing pranayama daily is essential to regulate, cleanse, activate and purify your pranic life force energy!

In yoga, Ayurveda and holistic medicine, it is believed that when your prana becomes unbalanced, you become susceptible to illness and disease in body, mind, and spirit. By bringing awareness to your body and consciously practicing breath control exercises, you can bring positive changes to your physical, mental, emotional, and spiritual well-being.

Alternate Nostril Breathing, Nadi Shodhana

Alternate nostril breathing is a specific practice to balance Ida and Pingala, masculine and feminine, right and left. This breath is where you intentionally inhale through one nostril and then exhale out the other nostril. It may be done either with the fingers holding a nostril closed or simply with the intentionality of the mind moving the channels of energy while you breathe.

You may practice breathing in one side and out the same side only for either awakening or helping to get sleepy. Inhaling left, exhaling right for a solar effect; inhaling right exhaling left a lunar effect.

According to the yogis, when the breath continues to flow in one nostril for more than two hours, as it does with most of us, it will have an adverse effect on our health. If the right nostril is involved, the result is mental and nervous disturbance. If the left nostril is involved, the result is chronic fatigue and reduced brain function. The longer the flow of breath in one nostril, the more serious the illness will be.

With this exercise, we breathe through only one nostril at a time. In normal every day breathing one alternates from one nostril to the other at various times during the day. In a healthy person the breath will alternate between nostrils about every 90 minutes to two hours. Because most of us are not in optimum health, this time period varies considerably between people and further reduces our vitality. Take a day and check throughout the day which nostril is dominant.

The name alternate nostril breathing is due to the fact that we alternate between the two nostrils when we do the breathing. Yogis believe that this exercise will clean and rejuvenate your vital channels of energy, thus the name nadi sodhana, meaning purification of nadis or channels of energy. The pronunciation is (nah-dee show-DAH-nah) meaning nadi = channel and shodhana or sodhana = cleaning, purifying.

Mrigi Mudra

To practice alternate nostril breathing sit in a comfortable asana and make Mrigi Mudra, hand to nose gesture folding down the index and middle finger and holding up the thumb. Beginning pranayama students may have some difficulty holding their raised elbow out to the side in position for the length of the practice. You can put a bolster across your legs and use it to support your elbow.

How to practice Nadi Shodhana

Make hand to Nose Gesture Mudra by holding out your right hand and folding in your index and middle finger, use the thumb and ring finger only during this practice. Take your right hand with the mudra and gently close your right nostril with your right thumb. Lift the elbow out to the side. Sit tall. Inhale through your left nostril, and then close it with your ring-little fingers. Keep your elbow up and out, creating space in the rib cage. Open and exhale slowly through the right nostril.

Keep the right nostril open, inhale, then close it with the thumb and exhale slowly through the left. This is one cycle. Continue, only switching on the exhales. Repeat at least 3 to 5 times on each side ending with an exhale through the opposite side you began with.

There are many combinations of alternate nostril breathing. One of the simplest techniques I teach regularly is as follows:

- Make the Mrigi Mudra for the Hand to Nose Gesture with the right hand, using the thumb and ring fingers only, begin careful not ot pinch the nose. Alternatively, if your folded fingers feel in the wayt, you may bring the first and middle fingers of the right hand to the third eye and use the thumb and ring fingers to close the nostrils alternating.

- Gently close off the right nostril with the thumb, do an inhalation from one nostril, and then slide the elbow out to the side.

- Close off the left nostril with the ring finger and exhale out from the right side.

- Inhale on same side and close off with the thumb and exhale out the left.

- This is called one round of alternate nostril breathing. At least three rounds on each side are generally done to complete the pranayama.

This is one round. After several rounds release the hand mudra and go back to the natural breath. Notice the affects of alternate nostril breath, feel the balance created. Some yoga schools of yoga begin this sequence by first closing the left nostril and inhaling through the right; this order is prescribed in the Hatha Yoga Pradipika, 2.7-10.

Traditionally Nadi Shodhana includes breath retention, fixed ratio breathing, and the repetition of certain seed (Bij) mantras. For beginning pranayama students, it's best to focus only on the inhales and exhales.

When breathing exercises are practiced regularly it is said to lower heart rate and reduce stress and anxiety. This particular pranayama is done to synchronize the two hemispheres of the brain, Ida and Pingala. Pranayama is stated to cleanse and purify the subtle energy channels (nadis) of the body so the prana flows more easily during. As with all energy work approach the practice of all bandhas and mudras cautiously, with a sense of child like wonder. Look for the subtle and sublime changes. Keeping a journal may be a useful tool to begin to see the fruits of your practice.

Five Element Breathing

Five Element Breathing is a relaxing way to tap in to your Source. Use your natural breath. As you do the breath pattern for each element in turn, attune with the cosmic element and experience its qualities within you. Experience the purification of your being on all levels: physical, mental, heart, soul, spirit. Practice five breaths for each element, or more.

There are many qualities of each element, as well as several mudras associated with it. I have listed them here with the fingers used to symbolize that particular element. You may study and practice the mudras on your own for further research.

Earth

Ring Finger: Prithivi Mudra

Inhale nose, exhale nose

Qualities: nurturing, solidity.

Movement: spreading horizontally.

Color: yellow-brown.

Sense: touch

Water

Pinkie: Apas Mudra, Varuna Mudra

Inhale nose, exhale mouth

Qualities: fluidity, purifying, giving life.

Movement: downwards.

Color: green.

Sense: taste

Fire

Thumb: Agni Mudra, Surya Mudra

Inhale mouth, exhale nose.

Qualities: enthusiasm, transmutation.

Movement: upward.

Color: red.

Sense: smell

Air

Index Finger: Vayu Mudra

Inhale and exhale mouth

Qualities: freedom, releasing from constructs, cosmic identity.

Movement: zig-zag.

Color: blue.

Sense: hearing

Ether

Heaven | Middle: Akasha Mudra

Very fine breath inhaling and exhaling through the nose

Qualities: 'emotion of the soul'. Peace. Unity.

Movement: stillness.

Color: white.

Sense: sight.

Playing with the elements, calling in the directions and honoring the traditional indigenous, Native and Shamanic practices will take your life to a whole new level. I wish for you to explore, learn, grow and most of all enjoy this life. These practices are designed to help you understand who you really are in relation to your Highest Good.

Chapter 2

Yoga Sutras, Fire, Energy, Purification

A study on the Yoga Sutras,

Slokas 1.5-1.11

It is said that the joy of deeper meditation comes through uncoloring the mental obstacles that veil the true Self, or the diamond within. Yoga was defined in the Yoga Sutras by Patanjali in sutras 1.1-1.4. Nowadays, we are in the process of experiencing the goal of Yoga. What may that be? We are talking beyond the physical benefits, the real Truth of the yoga practice is Self-realization, and this begins in this section of the Sutras.[15]

Vikalpa, Uncoloring Our Thoughts

First, lets look at what obstacles we may have in Self Realization. In yoga there are identified the five kinds of interfering thoughts or mental impressions (1.4) that block the realization of the true Self (1.3):

1) knowing correctly

2) incorrect knowing

3) imagination

 deep sleep, and

4) memory (1.5, 1.6).

---

[15] http://swamij.com/yoga-sutras-10511.htm

The Yogi learns to witness these five kinds of thoughts with non-attachment (1.15-1.16), discriminate between these five, and to cultivate the first type of thought, which is knowing correctly (1.7).

They are colored or not colored: These thought patterns may be colored (klishta) or not-colored (aklishta) (1.5). That coloring has to do with ignorance, I-ness, attachments, aversions, and fears (2.3). The simple observation of whether thought patterns are colored or not colored is an extremely useful part of the process of purifying, balancing, stabilizing, or calming the mind so that deeper meditation can come.

Witnessing, exploring, and uncoloring: By learning to explore and become witness to these five types of thoughts, and by learning to allow the coloring to fade (1.16) through the various processes of Yoga meditation, the veil over Truth gradually thins (1.2), and we come to experience our true Self (1.3).

Most important concept: This uncoloring process is an extremely important concept, and is further dealt with in the later chapters (2.1-2.9, 2.10-2.11). It is such an important concept that it is virtually impossible to practice Yoga without understanding it. (See also the articles on Uncoloring your Colored Thoughts and Witnessing Your Thoughts)

1.5 Those gross and subtle thought patterns (vrittis) fall into five varieties, of which some are colored (klishta) and others are uncolored (aklishta).

vrittayah pancatayah klishta aklishta

- vrittayah = the vrittis are
- pancatayah = five fold (and of two kinds); panch means five
- klishta = colored, painful, afflicted, impure; the root klish means to

cause trouble; (klesha is the noun form of the adjective klishta)

• aklishta = uncolored, not painful, not afflicted, pure; not imbued with kleshas; the root a- means without or in the absence of; hence, without the coloring called klishta

There are five kinds of thoughts, colored or not colored. This sutra introduces the nature of the five kinds of thoughts, and the fact that they are either colored (klishta) or not colored (aklishta) suggests the entire process of Yoga. In that process you gradually, systematically set aside all of the false identities that cloud over the true Self. This uncoloring process is an extremely important concept. Some thoughts are colored with attraction or aversion, while some other thoughts are uncolored or neutral.

Meanings of klishta and aklishta are a significant study. The reason for emphasizing the translation of colored and uncolored is that it can more directly be perceived as related to the thought patterns (vrittis) that are the stuff of which the clouds over the Self are made. The words klishta and aklishta are a pair of words that are in contrast with one another. With the 'a' in front of klishta, it becomes aklishta, so colored (klishta) becomes uncolored (aklishta). Translating these as colored and not colored gives a certain meaning, or feel to the words. In other words, the vritti, thought, is colored by the klishta process, so to speak. It is like the way an adult coloring book picture might be colored by a particular colored pencil (klishta). Framing the idea this way also suggests the solution, which is to remove the coloring (aklishta).

Several other word pairs have been used to describe klishta and aklishta, and each adds a certain flavor to the meaning. When holding the notion of colored and uncolored for klishta and aklishta, it might be useful to remember these other word pairs as well:

74

- klishta - aklishta
- painful - not painful
- not useful - useful
- afflicted - not afflicted
- impure - pure
- troubled - not troubled
- negative - positive
- vice - virtue
- unenlightened - enlightenment
- bondage - freedom

The first four sutras described how we come to know our true Self, and explained that when we are not experiencing that Reality, we are identified with, or entangled with the many levels and layers of our mental content. These entanglements are all part of these five thought patterns, whether being one, or some combination of the five. They are either colored or uncolored.

Thoughts are gross or subtle: These thought patterns are not just the day to day thoughts we experience; this notion of thought patterns (vrittis) is both gross and also extremely subtle. The meaning becomes gradually clearer with practice of the methods.

Witnessing the coloring: To observe the coloring of our thought patterns is one of the most useful practices of Yoga, and can be done throughout the day. This meditation in action, or mindfulness, can be of tremendous value in clearing the clouded mind, so that during your seated meditation time, that practice can go much deeper.

How to witness coloring: To observe the coloring of thoughts simply means that when a thought and its emotion arises, you simply say that, "This is colored," or "This is not colored." Similarly, to notice whether some decision or action is useful or not useful brings great control over your habits of mind. It is simply observing, and saying to yourself, "This is useful," or "This is not useful."

The process of uncoloring: Yoga rests on the two foundations of Abhyasa and Vairagya (practice and non-attachment; sutras 1.12-1.16). Then the seer rests in its True nature (1.3). Here, the subtler means of dealing directly with those attachments is introduced, by observing that the five kinds of thought patterns are either klishta or aklishta, colored or not colored. The process of uncoloring the deep impressions unfolds in stages. We need to gradually stabilize the mind and weaken the colorings, so that we might start to get some glimpses of that which is beyond all of those thought impressions and their colorings.

To better understand the process, take a look at the Chapter Outlines, which include the following from the Yoga Sutras of Patanjali:

- Efforts and commitment (1.19-1.22)
- Obstacles and solutions (1.30-1.32)
- Stabilizing and clearing the mind (1.33-1.39)
- Minimizing gross coloring (2.1-2.9)
- Dealing with subtle thoughts (2.10-2.11)
- Breaking the alliance of karma (2.12-2.25)
- The 8 rungs and discrimination (2.26-2.29)

The Five Kinds of Thought

1.6 The five varieties of thought patterns to witness are: 1) knowing correctly (pramana), 2) incorrect knowing (viparyaya), 3) fantasy or imagination (vikalpa), 4) the object of void-ness that is deep sleep (nidra), and 5) recollection or memory (smriti).

pramana viparyaya vikalpa nidra smritayah

- pramana = real or valid cognition, right knowledge, valid proof, seeing clearly
- viparyayah = unreal cognition, indiscrimination, perverse cognition, wrong knowledge, misconception, incorrect knowing, not seeing clearly
- vikalpah = imagination, verbal misconception or delusion, fantasy, hallucination
- nidra = deep sleep
- smritayah = memory, remembering

There are only five kinds of thoughts: Of all the countless thought impressions that come into the mind field, which form the matrix of the barrier or veil covering the true Self or center of consciousness, they all fall into one or more of these five categories. In other words, while there are many individual thought impressions, there are not countless types of thoughts to deal with, but only five. This can help greatly in seeing the underlying simplicity of the process of Yoga, not getting lost in the apparent multiplicity in the gross and subtle realms.

Witnessing the five kinds of thoughts: By learning to observe the thinking process, and then to discriminate between these five types of mental objects, we start to gain a mastery over them, and their ability to control our actions, speech, and thoughts.

Using Your Hand to Remember the Five Kinds of Thought

Starting with the thumb: Pramana, right; Vitaraya, wrong; Vikalpa, imagined or colored; Nidra, deep sleep; and Smriti, memory.

77

With mastery of witnessing: As that mastery comes within reach, we gradually find a neutral, non-attached (1.15, 3.38) stance of witnessing, where we can observe the entire flow of mind, while remaining peacefully undisturbed, unaffected, and uninvolved. Meditation can systematically deepen.

Without mastery of witnessing: Without that mastery, we become victims to our own unconscious mental process, losing free choice in external life as well as the ability to experience deep meditation.

Pramana is the one to cultivate: Of the five kinds of thought patterns, pramana, or correct knowledge is the one to cultivate. The process of continually seeing ever more clearly brings progress on the path of meditation. This process of seeing clearly, of seeing things as they are, is one of the ways of describing the inner journey, eventually revealing that absolute, unchanging True Self.

1.7 Of these five, there are three ways of gaining correct knowledge (pramana): 1) perception, 2) inference, and 3) testimony or verbal communication from others who have knowledge.

pratyaksha anumana agamah pramanani

- pratyaksha = direct perception or cognition
- anumana = inference, reasoning, deduction
- agamah = authority, testimony, validation, competent evidence
- pramanani = valid means of knowing, proofs, sources of correct knowing

Three ways to attain correct knowing: The first of the five kinds of thought patterns described in the last sutra is pramana, which is real or valid cognition, right knowledge, valid proof, seeing clearly. Here, in sutra 1.7, three different ways are described about how one acquires that correct knowing. These are direct perception, reasoning, and validation. Each of them are valid, and standing alone can provide correct knowing, though you want the three to be in agreement. This description of correct knowing applies both to mundane ways of knowing, such as seeing objects in the external world, and to spiritual insights on the inner journey.

Seek experience, not mere belief: In the oral Yoga tradition, it is said that you should not believe what you hear, but should seek direct experience. This is the meaning of the first of these three ways of knowing. The second part is that of reasoning, whereby you want that experience to be understood in the light of your own inference or reasoning. The third part is that you seek the validation through some respected authority or testimony. This might be a textual authority, such as the Yoga Sutras, or some respected person who has first hand knowledge.

Getting these three to converge: When you can get these three: experience, reasoning, and authoritative validation to all agree with one another, then you know, and you know that you know, in regard to any particular aspect of the inner journey. Thus, this sutra is an extremely practical tool for the inner journey.

What if the three have not converged?: Consider the alternatives of these three converging. Often, people will have some experience with their spiritual journey, and have no understanding of what has happened, nor any validation. This can be frustrating and fearful, and can leave one wandering, feeling lost for a very long time. If the experience were understood and validated, it could be integrated and used as a stepping stone to more advanced spiritual insights. If one has only logical reasoning, but no experience or validation, it can lead to mere intellectualizing. If one only has the authoritative knowledge, without personal understanding or experience, it can lead to cold memorization, such as can happen in academia or blind faith religion.

Seek each, and also convergence: For the sincere seeker, direct experience, reasoning, and validation are all three sought in relation to the inner journey, and in such a way that there is a convergence of the three.

1.8 Incorrect knowledge or illusion (viparyaya) is false knowledge formed by perceiving a thing as being other than what it really is.

viparyayah mithya jnanam atad rupa pratistham

- viparyayah = unreal cognition, indiscrimination, perverse cognition, wrong knowledge, misconception, incorrect knowing, not seeing clearly
- mithya = of the unreal, of the false, erroneous, illusory
- jnanam = knowing, knowledge
- atad = not its own, not that
- rupa = form, nature, appearance
- pratistham = based on, possessing, established, occupying, steadfast, standing

Incorrect knowing: Perceiving a thing as being other than what it really is.

A classic example of the shifting perception is the Rubin Vase, which is both a picture of a vase and a picture of two faces at the same time. Two classic examples are given by the Yogis for the misperception called viparyaya. First is the mistaking of a rope for a snake when the light is low, such as the twilight hours between day and night. The rope is always a rope, although the mind misperceives it in the moment. The second is similar, and is mistaking a post in the distance as being a man standing in the shadows.

80

Clearing many levels of misperception: During the inner journey of Yoga meditation, there are many currents and crosscurrents that are explored and examined (2.1-2.9, 2.10-2.11, 3.9-3.16, 4.9-4.12). One way of describing this process is that we are trying to see where we have made mistakes in perception (viparyaya), and are trying to see clearly (pramana, 1.7). Then we can transcend that object in the mind field, getting past the four forms of ignorance, or avidya (2.5), and experiencing our true Self (1.3).

Observe the misperceptions of daily life: If the reason we are not experiencing our true nature (1.3) is the clouding of false identities (1.4), then we want to become adept at noticing the ways in which we are not seeing clearly, so as to correct the misperceptions. For most of us, this process of mistaken identity is easily done in daily life.

Relationships with people: Recall how often you see some situation or person to be one way, only to later discover that there was some missing piece of information that changes your perception completely. For example, imagine you see a friend or co-worker who has a scowl rather than a smile, and whose attitude might seem negative towards you. That person may actually be angry from having had an argument with a family member, and the reaction had nothing to do with you.

Misperceptions can cause colorings! The problem with these misperceptions is that they can lead to the colorings, kleshas (1.5, 2.1-2.9). We see our world through rose colored glasses. You may have heard this old saying, this is referring to our kleshas or our perceptions. If there were simply misperceptions with no coloring, there would be no problem. The potential of the misperceptions of relationships with people, as my husband and I say, telling a story. The result might be increased egoism, attractions, aversions, or fears. Thus, we want our misperceptions (viparyaya) to become correct perceptions (pramana, 1.7).

81

1.9 Fantasy or imagination (vikalpa) is a thought pattern that has verbal expression and knowledge, but for which there is no such object or reality in existence.

shabda jnana anupati vastu shunyah vikalpah

- shabda = word, sound, verbal expression
- jnana = by knowledge, knowing
- anupati = following, in sequence, depending upon
- vastu = a reality, real object, existent
- shunyah = devoid, without, empty
- vikalpah = imagination, verbal misconception or delusion, fantasy, hallucination

There is no perceptible reality: Our minds are often thinking and creating chains of words and images. Often this process leads to thoughts or impressions that have no actual reality. The two kinds of thoughts discussed in the past two sutras both related to realities, whether seen clearly (1.7) or not clearly (1.8). However, vikalpa has no such corresponding reality, whether seen clearly or not.

Classic example: A classic example that the Yogis use is that of the horns of a rabbit. A rabbit does not have horns, although it can easily be conceptualized. The thought and the image are there, but there is no corresponding reality. Have you ever seen a jackalope? Well, in real life, yes, but was it real? Or was it a perception?

With objects and people it seems to be a habit of the human mind to form all sorts of fantasy ideas. We might fantasize having this or that thing, doing or saying something with some person, or creating in my story both the objects and the people. With the real objects and people in my world, I might even create these fantasy idea that these are really real and are mine. The mental impressions of the objects and people might be real (1.7) or misperceived (1.8), but the impressions related to the concept mine are complete fantasy, or vikalpa.

Often we speak of a thought process, which is one of living in the future. The mind is really taking the current thoughts, rearranging them this or that way, and then fantasizing some new combination as being the future, even though that fantasy is occurring in the present moment.

It is useful to reflect on the relationship between this fantasy process of mind and the four forms of ignorance (avidya) that are described in sutra 2.5.

While we are talking about how to deal with the thought patterns of the mind (1.2) so as to attain Self-realization or Samadhi (1.3), it is important to notate that these mental processes are not bad in the context of life and the world. The same fantasy or vikalpa that clouds over our true Self with the ego self is also the same creative mind that finds solutions to real life problems in the external world within our personality. It is even the vikalpa that creates the helpful lifestyle and environment in which we live so as to be able to do our meditations.

As our meditation practice deepens, we come to see ever more clearly that virtually our whole perception of external and internal reality is vikalpa, a product of imagination. Notice that even the root of the word imagination is image! Countless images are produced, stored, and then they arise. Even the subtleties of the five elements (earth, water, fire, air, space), the cognitive and active senses (indriyas), and the four functions of mind are products of this process of vikalpa.

The Object of Sleep

1.10 Dreamless sleep (nidra) is the subtle thought pattern which has as its object an inertia, blankness, absence, or negation of the other thought patterns (vrittis).

abhava pratyaya alambana vritti nidra

- abhava = absence, non-existence, non-occurrence, negation, voidness, nothingness
- pratyaya = the cause, the feeling, causal or cognitive principle, notion, content of mind, presented idea, cognition
- alambana = support, substratum, leaning on, dependent on, having as a base or foundation
- vritti = operations, activities, fluctuations, modifications, changes, or various forms of the mind-field
- nidra = deep sleep

Mind focuses on the object, which we call sleep. With this objectification it is as if sleep is a process whereby the mind is focusing on absence itself, as if that non-existence were an object itself. Metaphorically, it is as if the mind is focused on a black, fuzzy object that is set against a black field. There is something there for the mind to be focused on, yet, in the sense of what we normally consider to be a real object, there is nothing there.

Normally the mind focuses on some object. Nidra, or sleep, is the state where attention is focused on, or absorbed in that object of negation or voidness itself!

84

Sleep is the absence of the other four thought patterns. When any of the other though patterns are present (remember the hand exercise) then the mind is usually engaged or entangled in those images. When all four of them subside, or when the mind is not actively involved in these patterns, then comes the state of sleep. Alternatively, when one is free from all *five* of them, and still remains conscious, that is Samadhi, or total bliss and true enlightenment! As yogis we may get tiny glimpses of this state with dedication and practice.

Sleep is actually an object. This might seem to be insignificant, but it is actually important. Remember the principle in the first few sutras (1.2-1.4) that the reason we do not experience the eternal true Self, is that consciousness is always entangled with other objects. When we see that entering sleep is a process of focusing on still one more object, it becomes clearer why we want to remain in the waking state for meditation, while learning to let go of the intervening objects, including sleep, which is like that black, fuzzy object. In meditation, we focus on one object, intentionally, so that at some point we can let go of all objects, and experience the objectless state beyond all of the objects. This may sound confusing if you are new to the practice. Come back to this concept. Be encouraged this is a life long practice and we are always learning!

In another sense, sleep is a kind of level, not an object. When we translate these words of meditation from Sanskrit to English, we can end up with some confusion in the process. Nidra is most usually translated as sleep. However, in considering the levels of consciousness, the domains of gross, subtle, and causal, that deeper level is called prajna, which is a level of supreme (pra) knowledge (jna). This too is considered to be the level of deep sleep. So, we are using the word sleep in two compatible, though very different ways. If you know this, there is no confusion. The Yoga of the

Yoga Sutras is very practical, and here the emphasis is on contrasting the attention around this thought pattern (vritti) of sleep, as in contrast to the other four types of vrittis.

When we talk about mastering the mental process in relation to the entanglement with objects or fantasies, it can make sense, even at a more surface level. In relation to sleep, it is important to note that we want to move towards dis-identification even with that object, of sleep, just like we do with the other thought patterns. When we do the true Self comes shining through!

Do not mistake sleep, or nidra, for Samadhi. The higher level of Samadhi is without *any* object that has form, which has sometimes been described as void. Just to clarify, that Samadhi is very different than the void of other objects/thought patterns that comes with deep sleep. These are entirely different experiences.

1.11 Recollection or memory (smriti) is a mental modification caused by the inner reproducing of a previous impression of an object, but without adding any other characteristics from other sources. Memory can take on associations.

anubhuta vishaya asampramoshah smritih

- anubhuta = experienced
- vishaya = objects of experience, impressions
- asampramoshah = not being stolen, not being lost, not having addition
- smritih = memory, remembering

Memory is something with which we are very familiar; a previously stored impression simply awakens, stirs in the unconscious, and then springs forth into the conscious awareness, having pierced the veil between conscious and unconscious. We tend to make many assumptions, tell many stories, all based on false memory. [16] This is also seen as a Samskara, a pattern in thought, like a sandbank at the bottom of a lake. However, a rising memory often brings along with it many other memories, stirring up that sand. It then gets linked in such a way that the original memory is not seen in its pure form. In other words, the memory is being distorted/colored; it is commingled with the other types of thought patterns.

The memory being described here in this Sutra is the pure memory, without having stolen, or had additions from other memories or the creative, fantasizing, hallucinating thought process of mind. It is quite natural for these thought impressions to rise in the mind field. By discriminating between the types of thoughts, we can see which are simply memories, and which are memories that have become distorted and effectively turned into fantasies, which are vikalpa, described in sutra 1.9.

Mere memory is not so disturbing to our natural peace of mind. All of the other inner processes lead to the chitta-vritti, the mental process that blocks deep meditation. This is the monkey mind, the monkey chatter, in which we are all familiar. [17]

This practice of uncovering our thoughts is devoted to presenting the ancient path of the Self-Realization , in the tradition of the Himalayan masters, in simple, understandable and beneficial ways.

The goal of our Sadhana, or personal practice, is the highest Joy that comes from that Realization in direct experience of the center of truth, our consciousness, the Self, Source, Christ, the Atman or Purusha, which is one and the same with the Absolute Reality.

---

[16] For learning more on our assumptions read The Four Agreements by Don Miguel Ruiz
[17] https://blog.yogaglo.com/2013/11/the-language-of-yoga-chitta-vritti/

This Self-Realization comes through Yoga meditation of the Yoga Sutras, the contemplative insight. Utilizing the classical approaches of all four paths of yoga:

Raja, Jnana, Karma, and Bhakti Yoga

Also recommended in your daily Sadhana are the practices of Yoga: Hatha, Kriya, Kundalini, Vinyasa and Tantra Yoga. Within these practices meditation, contemplation, mantra and prayer converge into a unified force directed towards the final stage, piercing the pearl of wisdom, bindu, leading to the Absolute Truth. This is the ultimate reality.

Kundalini Energy as an Offering

90% of yoga therapy is waste removal.

~T.K.V. Desikichar

Kundalini is seen in many ways, some colored some uncolored. Kundalini is sometimes called a dormant spiritual energy. Kundalini is sometimes referred to as a spiritual energy. These are not Truth. In fact, Kundalini is an obstruction to Prana, all negative effects are advidya. Sri Krishnamacharya said, it MUST BE REMOVED, as in dealt with, or in yoga we say it must be thrown into the fire, the Agni. This process is for purification, Swaha, as an offering.[18]

The Apana Vayu

The Apana Vayu is the downward flow or energy; we will discuss the five directions of energy in depth at the end of this chapter. For now we will explore Apana and it's usage in purification.

Apana consists of the liquids, light, and gases absorb

---

[18] Leslie Kaminoff Yoga Anatomy, Lisa's notes from his master training on the book Anatomy of the Breath

Things accumulate:

- Not saving money, we don't get to it and debt builds up.

- Spring cleaning, this is much needed because stuff is not being moved out in normal activity, so it takes much extra effort to clean.

- Detoxing the body, one of my personal favorites, this is needed for everyone. We accumulate toxins from our lifestyle and cleansing is a necessary and absolutely essential practice. We will go into more detail on later in the book.

- Saving things, let's pause and look further at the history of stuff you save. First off, you can start by making a list. This is the beginning of a very real purification process.

The Fire Purification Process

What does that process of collecting, identifying, purging and releasing actually look like? Yes, there is a cycle:

- Attachment, the collection of the stuff

- Identifying, realizing the need to release the stuff

- Question, how to get rid of the stuff?

- IDEA: Transform it by Fire! This is the element of transmutation, Agni!

- Make it an offering, a Puja, a dedication of the burning process to something greater that you.

- Throw it into the fire.

- Release it. This a declaration! Said in Sanskrit: SWAHA! In Lakota: Aho! In western social media slang: Let that Shit Go!!!

Fireplaces are a great example of the purification process of accumulating and letting go of stuff, too. Think about the collection of wood to burn, the lighting process, the burning process, then the collection of soot, the accumulation of ashes and finally cleaning out the old ashes. Here is a good way to look at this analogy of a fireplace, compared to the Chakras and repiratory system of our human bodies.

1. Identify the need to purify
2. Open the flu
3. Clear your intention to make it an offering
4. Create an altar space.
5. Create an alter that is clean, set and cleared for the ritual
6. Build the fire
7. Get it going strong
8. Identify what you are going to burn
9. Dedicate what you are going to burn
10. Throw it in and watch it burn, release!

In this example the fireplace is the Solar Plexus. The Flu is the Sushuma channel of energy in which the Prana flows upward. The throwing it into flame, the offering it upward is the exhale, in complete surrender. Think of the direction the diaphragm moves on the exhale, upward flowing energy. Turning the flame downward and moving it to burn is the inhale, when the diaphragm moves down, in the direction of Apana.

This process is essential because squeezing and pushing all that stuff down is not working!!!

Puja by definition is the act of throwing something into the flame as an offering. When we practice puja we can take and remove what doesn't serve our Highest Good, offer it up to Self or Source and release it to be transformed into something beautiful.

PUT IT INTO THE FLAME! OPEN THE SPACE! LET IT BURN! SWAHA!

~Leslie Kaminoff, paraphrase from Anatomy of the Breath workshop

Chapter 3 Chakras, Mudras, Vayus, OM

In this chapter we will discuss the energy the mudras and the direction energy moves. We will not directly discuss the asanas or the postures. To begin let me address something; the energy or the sound of a word is important, especially in Sanskrit. The Sanskrit word 'asana' is pronounced 'ahhh-sana'. The ah sound is the first sound a baby makes, and the last sound we make when we cross over, and is the first letter in the Sanskrit alphabet. The inflection is on the 'ah' in the word asana. It is not pronounced 'aw-saaana'! To remember how to say this word in your mind and out loud, simply think of ahhhh, how lovely it feels to do yoga! We do not have space for a deep discussion on the benefits and photos of each significant yoga asana in this book. You can find this and all of the foundational and advanced asanas in my free eBook on our website, yoga4love.com. It is titled Yoga 4 Love's Big Book of Yoga Poses, Asana 101, 201 and 301. This was originally part of this book, but it is really a much needed tool separate from these teachings. So feel free to download that and use for your yoga practice, as well as a reference tool when I mention the poses mentioned here within!

Chakra Balancing Through Yoga Asana and Sound

The chakras are the energy points in the human body. Each of the 7 centers are located in the 7 prime areas that have many nerve endings, as well as the important energetic connections we will discuss later.

We will focus first on practice for the balancing for all 7 Chakras. [19] For each of these practices it is recommended to hold at least one to three

---

[19] adapted from Jeff Migdow, M.D. 1998, Lisa's friend and published author, used with permission

minutes while focusing on your yogic breath. Build up to longer holds and longer meditations associated with each chakra.

1. Root Chakra, Muladhara: Standing poses using legs, Frog

2. Sacral Chakra, Swadhisthana: Bhujangasana/Cobra Wave

3. Solar Plexus Chakra, Manipura: Utkatasana/Chair pose

4. Heart Chakra, Anahata: Goddess, any asanas with arms, Kundalini arm movements

5. Throat Chakra, Vishudha: Matsyasana/ fish or Setu Bandhasana/ bridge

6. Third Eye Chakra, Ajna: Practicing yoga mudras for the Third Eye is the first stage. Mudras are special hand positions believed by yogis to have the power to direct more energy to specific chakras. [20] To enhance the effect for third eye activation, simultaneously chant the Om. Savangasana, shoulder stand, is the next stage and more advanced. Matsyasana, fish pose, with throat open and poised on the crown of the head while looking upside-down is the most powerful pose for pineal opening, and this is the highest stage.

7. Crown Chakra, Sahasrara: practice the Yoga Mudra (either Lotus or Vira), hold mudra above top of head.

Chanting 101

By visualizing or focusing on your third eye while chanting is an especially powerful tool for directing your inner energies to activate your third eye. Many schools of thought claim that by using the focal point at the inside of the brain at the midway point between the pineal gland and the pituitary body, a vibrating magnetic field can be created around the pineal gland. One way to accomplish this is to chant certain sounds during your

---

[20] http://www.awaken-consciousness.com/blog/2016/01/12/15-ways-to-open-your-third-eye/

third eye visualization, or while meditating on or gazing at an image of the third eye chakra.

Balancing Chakras with Crystals and Reiki

Crystals are helpful tools for balancing chakras. There are so many great resources on which crystals are for which chakra that we not spend an entire chapter on this. I daily practice with my crystals and am ever expanding my collection as well as my knowledge on the crystal kingdom and the stone people. We, for the sake of this book, will move on and I encourage you to google and do research this topic on your own. Just know that in almost every healing session I do I use crystals and my collection of my little friends is one of my most prized material possessions. Crystals are very powerful! They literally hold and recalibrate energy. Just think about your watch or your computer, the silicon chip literally is a crystal. Our US Navy is even teaching our sailors about the power and useage of crystals and energy.

Here are a few ways to utilize crystals in the balancing of the chakra system:

- Feel out which chakras are strongest and weakest, you can use crystals or you can simply use your hands. Start by scanning the body, first close the physical body, then scanning in layers. Next scan the emotional body, about six inches out, then scan the energy body about a foot out, then the wisdom body, then finally the bliss body at arms length. This is helpful to do while using Reiki. Your energy will be larger than arm's length.

- Simply intend to send your healing to these outer expanded layers, and deep into the atoms of the body and the DNA! Placing a crystal on a certain area of the body or in a particular pattern can be very helpful. Intend your healing to go to these inner or outer layers. You need not physically reach all the areas you are working with. Intention is the key.

Once you find a strong chakra and a weaker or less attuned chakra use this simple technique to balance it. You can do this on yourself or others. You need not be a Reiki healer, again trust and work with intention in the Light of Christ Consciousness, or however you refer to your Highest Self.

- Place left hand over strongest chakra
- Place right hand over weakest
- As you inhale feel prana, energy, chi, ki moving from strongest energy center flowing into your left hand.
- As you exhale feel prana flowing from left hand to right and down into weakest energy point.
- Add Bij sounds (see chart below) by chanting, connecting vowel sounds from the strongest to the weakest, blending the sounds. For example if the third chakra is the strongest in your scan and the fifth is the weakest, then chant Aaahhhhh-eeeeee, bringing energy from third into the fifth. This may feel strange, if you are not used to chanting or moving energy. Trust. Let it flow. Continue to chant the strongest vowel sound into weakest vowel sound feeling energy flowing up into the left hand, into right and down into weakest until chakra feels balanced.
- When balanced, stop, put down your arms, breathe and relax.
- Great work!

Mala Beads and the Sacred Number 108

I use mala beads for my chanting and healing practice. I own many of different stones and crystals, and when practiced regularly you can literally build the energy of a specific intention or mantra into your mala. This helps greatly with your meditation, elevation of your energy and the ability to get back into a higher frequency faster and with less resistance.

94

Most malas created are in a count of 108. This is a sacred number. What is sacred about the number 108, you may ask? Here is some wonderful examples from science and sacred texts:

- The diameter of the Sun is 108 times the diameter of the Earth.
- The distance from the Sun to the Earth is 108 times the diameter of the Sun.
- The average distance of the Moon from the Earth is 108 times the diameter of the Moon.
- In Ayurveda, there are 108 Marmas. points that are vital for giving life to living beings.
- The Sri Yantra, one of the most powerful symbols in sacred geometry intersects in 54 points each with a masculine and feminine quality, totaling 108.
- In Vedic astrology or Jyotish, there are 12 houses and 9 planets. 12 times 9 equals 108.
- In Tantra, it is estimated that every day on average a human breathes 21,600 times out of which 10,800 are solar energy and 10, 800 are lunar energy. Multiplying 108 X 100 is 10,800.
- The famous saint Bharata, considered the father of Indian theatrical art forms, wrote the 'Natya Shastra' which has 108 movements of the hand and feet .
- There are 54 letters in the Sanskrit alphabet. Each can be mentioned as a masculine (Shiva) and feminine (Shakti) aspect, totaling to 108.
- The Upanishads. The Muktikā Upanishad's lists 108 Upanishads.
- Heart Chakra: The chakras are the intersections of our nerves and our energy system's prana life force energy lines. There are said to be a total of 108 energy lines converging to form the heart chakra. One of

them, sushumna leads to the crown chakra, and is said to be the path to Self-realization. [21]

Bij Sounds, Seed Sounds, First to Seventh Chakras

Bij Mantra sounds are used to spin chakras and build energy. Use sound Moving up the Chakras to the crown to invoke Prana, use crown down to root to invoke grounding.

A great Chakra Mala that I like use has seven stones for each chakra, counting from root to crown, with a quartz between for 56. At the guru bead (the one with the tassel) there are 12 amethyst. [22] To use this I chant the seed Bij sounds for each with a short OM between with each crystal bead. This is 56 beads, then you go from crown back down to root on the last rounds with the Bij sound chanting. Each mala has 108 beads. Each round of 108 is one round. You can do one, 10 or up to 108 rounds. There are literally hundreds of types of malas. Many malas have different stones or crystals. Find one you really resonate with to start your practice.

I believe you will love this practice of Bij Chakra chant meditation. We have this chant as a free audio file on our website, yoga4love.com/audio-video called 'Live Chant for the Chakras'. Pull that up online if you are unsure how to do this chant. [23] I love this chant, and intend that you will become attuned to the feeling of each sound in each energy point very quickly. Give it a try now! It's really fun! The thing about chanting is you have to be all in, whispering a chant is so less effective. You want to create resonance and vibration, so go on, belt it out!

- Lam
- Vam
- Ram

---

[21] https://www.quora.com/Why-is-the-number-108-considered-sacred-by-Hinduism
[22] http://atmasofferings.com/product/vedic-chakra-mala/
[23] http://yoga4love.com/audio-video/

- Yam
- Ham
- Om (short)
- Ooommmm (Aum)

Each of these sounds is a seed sound (Bij sound) for one of the seven main chakra centers in the body. Starting at the root, Lam; Sacral, Vam; Solar Plexus, Ram; Heart, Yam; Throat, Ham; Third Eye, Om; to the Crown, OM.

Practice moving the energy from root to crown with your sound. For homework (or hOMework) we do a focus on each of the chakras in our Yoga 4 Love Advanced Training Programs and have a recorded YouTube video on each, with a handout for each chakra on our blog.

Each chakra also has a higher sound, just like moving up the scales on a piano. Use the higher octave vowel sounds to help move energy and release tension. These higher sounds are listed moving up the chakras from root to the crown. This can be a very simple chant. Try it now! Commit and just go for it... have you heard the phrase dance like no one is watching? Well let's just chant like no one is listening!

- Oh
- Oo
- Ah
- Ay
- Ee
- Mm
- ing

Final Chakra Balancing

Once you practice balancing with sound and crystals you may want to do a final clearing. This is a great tune up for you or anyone you are working with[24].

- Start at Muladhara, Root 1, work up to Sahasrara, Crown, 7.
- Repeat the Bij sound for each chakra. Tune in. Feel the area with your hand on the body then scan the body root to crown with holding the hands a few inches away. Notate any warmth, coolness, tingling and any sensations. Using Reiki begin healing the area. This is a very helpful tool here. We all have this gift, we just need to listen and feel.
- Chant the BIJ sound four times out loud, then pause. Listen and hear the reverberation and internal sound vibration.
- Intone the Chakra vowel sound.
- Feel area again.
- Compare the chakras already completed and balanced for strength or weakness.
- When you feel totally balanced pause, breathe and relax.
- Rest and tell yourself 'Great work'.
- Take a Savasana.

Hand Mudras For Pranayama, Breath Control

For the practice of certain pranayamas, breathing exercises, particularly those which require the regulation of the breath through one specific nostril or the other, special hand positions, or mudras, are employed. These are referred to as the prana, or energy, hasta, or hand, mudras. Let's look into this a bit more, shall we?

---

[24] Given by Dr. Jeff Migdow, with permission, adapted

Mudras, are truly yoga for the hands. Mudras are literally creating Prana life force energy with your hands and most importantly your intenton. It is an energetic connection to a symbol that has been used with deep intention for thousands of years! There are some Mudra apps and many great books on this topic. I encourage you to look up the Mudras we reference here as you read along.

The Prana Hasta Mudras

These energic positions for hands are exact finger positions within the mudras used to stimulate specific nerve points. These points are called nadi bindus, or energetic points. They are literally points that lie within the energy body layer of the five bodies. The energy bodies lie a few inches to a foot to several feet, up to several hundred yards in highly practiced individuals. These five energy bodies are called Koshas. The layer we are working with in the breath and hand mudras here is called the Pranamaya Kosha. To break Sanskrit down is really logical and simple; prana is energy, maya is 'magic' or 'illusion', a fundamental concept in yogic philosophy,[25] and kosha is the reference to the layer in the aura.

These 'hand energy gestures', or Mudras, become increasingly useful as one progresses to higher levels of the pranayama, breath control, practices. However, even in the early stages of practice it is important to pay particular attention to these mudras as well, and to be meticulous in their proper performance in order to gain the greatest benefits now and later on. Be clear that the hand positions are truly very specific energetic conductors and it is important to correct them. Do not allow 'sloppy' or weak mudras, as they are a disservice to the energetic cleansing action, or kriya, you are doing or teaching.

Each of the pranayama mudras are practiced using the right hand. Note for yoga teachers: when teaching in front of a class using the mirroring

---

[25] https://www.britannica.com/topic/maya-Indian-philosophy

technique is always best for beginners, because inevitably when you have rapport they will mimic you. So, you will be doing the mudra on the left when facing the class. For your personal practice, of course, use the right hand.

Mudras, General Directives: if the arm should tire in the beginning, the left hand can be used to support the right elbow or you can stack up bolsters and pillows. The nostrils should be closed gently, without excessive pressure or   pinching. The head should be held up, chin level with the horizon, and facing directly forward, with the eyes closed. Take an internal drishdi; this is the focal point discussed at the third eye chakra, most usually.

Hand to Nose Gesture, Nasarga Mudra

- The easiest to master of the two most common mudras practiced in the various alternate nostril breathing techniques of yoga is the nasarga mudra. Nasika means nose in Sanskrit.
- The second and third fingers, the index and middle, of the right hand are bent down at the knuckles and folded in. We do not use these fingers in our as they are symbolic of ego and fire, respectively.
- Place the other two fingers extended out and the thumb open.
- If the bend in fingers get in the way another option is to place index and middle fingertips on the third eye in the mudra.
- The tip of the thumb is used to close the right nostril.
- The fourth and fifth fingers (ring and pinkie) are used to close the left nostril.

Watch out for the habit of reverting to using the strongest fingers, the index or middle, or pinching the nose. Do not allow incorrect mudras to become habitual in your own practice.

Mudra to Balance Feminine and Masculine, Ida and Pingala

- The third fingertip (middle finger) is placed, with light pressure, against the upper root of the nose, between the brows.
- The index finger is used to close the right nostril.
- The fourth finger (ring finger) is used to close the left nostril. Note for ladies; this works well, unless you have really long nails!
- The remaining first and fifth fingers (thumb and pinkie) are splayed open, forming a 'V' shape.

These two fingers are directed to the points to balance both sides of the energy body. The Ida is the left side, and the Pingala is the right side. The nadis are energy channels in which the energy moves within the energy and physical body. By balancing the Ida and Pingala we in turn we balance the central channel. the Sushuma channel, indirectly.

Mudras, Hand, Face and Body Expression

A symbol in the wider sense of gesture or action....a symbol expressed with the hands to state for oneself and others the quality of different moments of meditation...

~Chogyam Trungpa,

A Tibetan Buddhist who founded many spiritual centers in the West

In Sanskrit, mudra means posture, or seal. While some mudras involve the entire body, most are performed with the hands and fingers, and are commonly defined as systematic hand gestures for non-verbal modes of communication and spiritual self-expression. Mudras are external expressions of inner resolve, suggesting that such nonverbal communications are more powerful than the spoken word.

There is much theory behind mudra practice. It is stated that Mudras attract cosmic energy into the microcosm through the Law of Attraction, as well as the energy of thousands of years of intention before us. They arouse the etheric body's dormant energy into awakening! These awakened energies manifest as magnetic and electrical force, depending on their form. Like the physical body, the etheric layers of the body has its own nervous system, or channels, conveying prana, life force energy. In yoga teachings, these channels or maps are called Nadis.

According to a very reputable online education site, Anatomy Trains, the facia plays a huge role in energy. Current speculation and many hypotheses suggest that these channels are directly related to the facia. Super interesting studies are being held on the facia. So what is facia, you may wonder? Fascia is the biological fabric that holds us together, the connective tissue network. You are about 70 trillion cells made up of neurons, muscle cells, epithelia, all humming in relative harmony. Fascia is the 3D spider web of fibrous, gluey, and 'Fasciawet' proteins that binds them together in their proper placement.[26] Every mudra is designed to clear some of these nadis from impurities and psychic toxins.

Benefits of Mudra Practice and the Science Behind Mudras

Mudras benefit the mind, breath, thoughts, as well as the bio-magnetic fields, referred to as auras or koshas, in a variety of ways.

- Health: The power of mudras clears the subtle channels and psychic centers in the five koshas, the layers of the body, allowing life force

---

[26] https://www.anatomytrains.com/fascia/

or Prana, to flow unhampered to the organs and all parts of the body.[27]

- I.Q. improvement: As the physical cleansing process takes place, clarity of mind is attained. The mental faculties are considerably enhanced, making it possible for the cosmic soul-intelligence to express itself with greater intensity and clarity.

- Enhancing and expanding the aura: The magnetism produced by the mudras cleanses the bio-magnetic field of the body. This practice empowers the all five of the koshas with greater vitality. The practice also forms a protective shield or bubble, if you will, against negative energies.

- Enlightenment and Consciousness: As a result of the cleansing process and the activation of Shakti, the Divine feminine creative principle, in the form of kundalini energy, one's consciousness is transformed, transcending ordinary awareness.

- Acquisition of the powers attainments of the Masters: The ancient hatha yoga and Buddhist texts, the Gherand Sanhita and the Vajrayana Tantra, advise that the practice of mudras can gift the practitioners great powers and psychic abilities, called siddhis.

- Transformation and regeneration: The overall effect of the *consistent* practice of mudras is the complete transformation and regeneration of the mind, body and Spirit with the ultimate benefit of the spiritual expansion of the Consciousness.

Are you ready for this journey? I say sign me up! The human body is made up of five elements, Earth, Water, Fire, Air and Ether or Space. According to Dr. Matthew J Taylor in a commentary of the Continuing Yoga

---

[27] Dr. Indu Arora author of Yoga: Ancient Heritage, Tomorrow's Vision; Excerpt from The Science of Yoga, page 432

Education of Smart Safe Yoga he states, "(At the) Asian Hall at the British Museum in London the presence of nearly every statue exhibiting at least one mudra confirmed my suspicion: We in the West have overlooked a powerful technology of yoga. It was no accident that the hall was filled with silent demonstrations of what I predict will become part of the next wave in smart, safe yoga."

Mudras are intentional and purposeful body positions, most often involving the hands, but not exclusively. These positions are said to offer the practitioner insight, powerful healing, states of higher consciousness and physical stabilizing capabilities. The modern Western asana-based yoga has largely skipped over these techniques in favor of the more culturally familiar yoga poses with a cardiovascular or fitness theme. The mudra offers a subtle perspective of going within, and sadly has been most conveyed as an occasional meditation prop at best in most brands of yoga. [28]

To learn more about the mudras and how they can affect the body, mind connection let's again use our hand [29]. Remember we are all made up of five elements, and on a side note we are actually mostly space, also referred to as ether, or Akasha, in Sanskrit.

In this example each finger represents one of the five elements:

- Thumb (Fire): The thumb is the symbol of Divine energy, the Prana life force energy that flows through our bodies unconditioned by our subconscious patterning or karmic complexities. The thumb is the symbol of will power, the power that can be drawn upon by our willing (not willfulness) consciousness.

- Index finger (Air): The index finger is the symbol of our ego personality. It symbolizes energies controlled by unconscious mind patterns, and when controlled by the conscious in a positive way,

---

[28] http://smartsafeyoga.com/the-power-and-science-of-mudra/
[29] www.yogsadhna.com

these energies produce expansion. It is also known as the 'Jupiter' finger.

- Middle finger (Ether/Space/Akasha): The middle finger is the most karmic or the most conditioned energies. This finger is utilized only in those mudras that require heavy, stabilizing forces. It symbolizes the Saturn force.
- Ring finger (Earth): The ring finger symbolizes the Sun's energies. These energies relate to the strength of an individual.
- Pinkie finger (Water): The little finger emanates energies that are important in the unfolding of the intellect and of business. It is known as the Mercury finger.

When combining the finger placements in different ways, forming different mudras, they ultimately balance the ratio and proportion of that element in the body. It is also important to note that *how* you press the finger or thumb creates different effects on that element. When pressed at the tip, the element is increased. When pressed under thumb, the element is neutralized. When pressed at the base of the finger, the element is decreased. Mudras can be practiced for a minimum of 30 seconds (five or so breaths) building up to 45 minutes daily, for achievement of desired effects. The practice can be spread out over three times a day for convenience or depending on your own intention, determination and discipline. Let your intuition be your guide here. It will tell you when you are ready to stop or whether to continue with a succeeding mudra, if required.

Therapeutic Mudras for Each of the Five Elements
Vayu Mudra, Air Element

To perform this mudra, first fold the index finger into the hand at the base of the thumb. Press the back of second knuckle with the thumb. Keep the other three fingers together and reasonably straight. You can perform this mudra in any sitting, standing, lying down position or even when walking. You can perform it any time of the day, on an empty or full stomach.

It is important to note that like the element of air. this mudra works in peaks and valleys (it decreases, then increases). Therefore, once you have achieved the desired benefit, although subtle, stop the practice. With more practice the benefits will become more apparent.

This mudra is said to release excess wind energy from the stomach and other parts of the body, releasing aches and pains and acting as first aid. It also is said to help with arthritis pains, gout, paralysis, Parkinson's disease, chest pains, any pain associated with excess wind in the body or any other imbalance of the air element.

Agni Mudra, Fire Element

Fold the ring finger to the base of thumb and press it with the thumb at the second knuckle. Keep the rest of the three fingers straight. For this mudra hold for at least 15 minutes at a stretch, and practice two to three times daily for best results. Practice this mudra on an empty stomach and in a sitting position only. Never perform this mudra on a full stomach. Pay attention to your body, this practice is subtle. Discontinue the mudra in case of any acidity, heartburn or indigestion This mudra is said to have many benefits such as helping dissolve extra body fat by balancing the metabolic rate. It may prevent and control obesity, burn excess phlegm and help compensates for sluggish digestion. It also may help to increase body strength and with regular practice it may reduce tension and even could lower cholesterol levels. One more immediate benefit is that it provides heat and energy to the body and is excellent to do in winter. The overall practice decreases the earth element in the body.

Prithivi Mudra, Earth Element

To practice this mudra simply touch the tip of the thumb and the tip of the ring finger together, keeping the other three fingers straight. Make sure you do not force the fingers to be straight, only try to keep them so. It is always a good option to do mudra practice with both hands at the same time, although it is not a rule. This mudra is preferably practiced in the morning, but can be performed any time of the day and for any duration. You can do this mudra when you feel sluggish or are lacking energy, and when practiced regularly it can help with increasing enthusiasm and motivation in life. Perform this mudra with both hands by sitting in sukasana (cross-legged) or padmasana, Lotus pose. Rest the backs of the arms on the legs and the elbows straight, palms facing up for receiving, palms facing down for grounding. This mudra has many great assets. It is said to helps boost the blood circulation. It can, with practice and intention, increases tolerance and patience. We can all use that! Great news is that this mudra helps in meditation. This mudra is an association of the Earth with the power of the Sun, therefore it brings solidity to the body. For instance it may help to assists in weight gain if the body is weak or too lean. It may help restore the balance and equilibrium of the body and can ward off weakness, fatigue and dullness. It increases prana in the body and therefore increases and brightens the aura. Another wonderful benefit is that it activates the thinking power of the mind and helps to broaden the orthodox and conservative thinking patterns.

Varun mudra, Water element

You may perform this mudra at any time of the day in a sitting, standing or lying down position, although the best pose is sitting sukasana, cross-legged seated pose. Join the pinkie fingertip with the tip of the thumb, keeping the rest of the fingers straight and together. Do not press the tip of the little finger near the nail as it causes dehydration rather than hydrating the system, rather press the pads of the finger and thumb. This is an important mudra as up to 60% of the human adult body is water. [30]

---

[30] https://water.usgs.gov/edu/propertyyou.html

Think of what you need to survive, really just survive. air, then water and food... and maybe social media next?

For this mudra we are going to concentrate on water here. Water is of major importance to all living things. Up to 60% of the human adult body is water. Varun is the name for a water god, so this mudra is named after this archetype. It balances the water element in the body, it moisturizes the body and can also be used as a thirst-quenching mudra, as it activates the salivary glands. It is said to aid in healing stomach infection, kidney malfunction and helps promote proper urination. It also is said to activates the circulation of fluids in the body. Ancient text suggest it purifies the blood and heals many blood disorders. By helping fluidity it can releases constipation. By activating the water element this mudra brings luster and glow to the body, especially the face and can be excellent for skin, helping reduce wrinkles, skin infections and dryness.

Akasha Mudra, Ether Element

How to practice this mudra? Join the tip of the middle finger with the tip of the thumb, keep the rest of the three fingers intentionally straight with energy. You may perform this mudra any time of the day and for any duration, however the best time is in the morning, before eating, right alert waking. Sitting in sukhasana, easy seated, or padmasana, lotus, try to hold this mudra for up to 45 minutes, though you may start with a much shorter time period, depending on discipline and practicality of your practice time. This mudra is a combination of the ether element with the sun. It pertains to any ailment involving sound. It is excellent for increasing the sensitivity to hear sounds.

OM, The Sound of the Universe (p 108!)

To place this kind of sound in perspective I am referring to the sound without a sound, the sound of the Universe. Imagine a time before the Universe existed and all there was was a field of Pure Consciousness, an eternal silence. This was not an empty silence, but one filled with the potential for everything! At some point, Pure Consciousness, or Source, wanted to have an experience. [31] Since nothing else existed, it could only experience itself. All experiences are based on contrast, so Source, or Pure Consciousness, had to move within itself to experience itself. Movement creates friction, friction creates noise, so Source created a sound. Source, by definition, is silent. This sound was OM, and it had to be forced out of the silence. It became what we call 'conditioned consciousness' as it is called, according to the Chora Center. The OM, or conditioned consciousness, is what we experience as the Universe in which we live.

To continue a bit off topic of the mudra, but on topic of the sound of the OM, which is also referred to as the Cosmic Consciousness, the idea that God created the world out of nothing is central today to many cultures including Islam, Christianity, and Judaism. There are many references to a god creating the Universe by sound being spoken into existence. In the Young's Literal Translation bible Genesis 1:3 says so perfectly, "and God saith, 'Let light be;' and light is."[32] The Gospel of John 1:1 states, "In the beginning was the Word, and the Word was with God, and the Word was God." The Word is the sound of OM and God is Oneness.

So back to the topic of mudras, according to Gertrud Hirschi, who was schooled in the traditional knowledge of this eastern art of healing and a well-known Swiss yoga teacher, she states that doing a Mudra "shows how these easy techniques can recharge personal energy reserves and improve quality of life. These mysterious healing gestures can calm the stress, aggravations, and frustrations of everyday life." [33] Akasha Mudra is extremely beneficial. It is aid to aid in calcium and phosphorus absorption from the diet and also their formation, which makes it

---

[31] https://chopra.com/articles/appreciating-om-the-sound-of-the-universe
[32] http://biblehub.com
[33] Book Mudras Yoga in Your Hands by Gertrud Hirschi

a very good mudra for those having weakness of bone, such as osteoporosis. It is a great mudra for releasing tension and can be used during meditation as it keeps the mind calm and serene. With regular practice you may be able to create calm and clarity and increase the ability to control the thought process.

Prana Mudra is a mudra for life force energy! To practice Prana mudra place the thumb, pinkie and ring finger together. Extend out the index and middle with energy!

The Prana mudra can be used whenever you feel drained or need an extra boost of energy. It is good to use in the morning to awaken and fully embrace the new day. It is also very powerful to use in chanting, Surya Namaskar, meditation on the sun, solar eclipses and change of seasons. It is especially good for setting and keeping your daily Sadhana practice alive and energetic!

The Five Vayus of Prana

Prana is literally our life force. Prana when spelled with a capital P refers to the Divine Source and prana with a lower case 'p' is the 'prana vayu'[34]. This vayu, or energy channel, runs from root chakra to crown about three centimeters in front of the spine, connecting us from Mother Earth to Father Sky. We stand between Earth and Sky as Two-Leggeds, as the Native American elders teach us. These teachings are vital as Shamanic Practitioners. This vayu is the subtle form of the Vata dosha, subtle meaning unable to be manipulated by our conscious efforts. The prana that moves in the central Shushuma channel can, gratefully, be manipulated in a more obscure and less direct way for our health and well being by many ancient and balancing practices described here within.

The five divisions sub-doshas, or constitutions, of Prana are five known Prana Vayus. Let us take a look at these five ways that energy moves! First, we need to learn about the places that life force energy is concentrated.

---

[34] from the teachings of Shiva Rea

These points are called Marmas. They are described as points on the body located where the junctions of the flesh, veins, arteries, tendons bones and joints meet. On a more etherial level these points are said to be where Vata, Pitta and Kapha meet and where Eternity and Relativity meet.[35]

prana Vayu (lower case p)

- Responsible for the heartbeat, absorption of nutrients and the breath. Prana (life force) enters the body through the nose and mouth, from here the oxygen is distributed to every cell through the body by the blood.
- Nature: Upward Flowing
- Seat: Head Marmas and Heart (to a lesser degree)
- Physical: Nerves
- Aspect: Solar, Masculine

Apana Vayu

- Responsible for the downward movements of prana, elimination of Malas-waste products from the body via the excretory systems, and the lungs
- Controls menstruation
- Governs Vatas site of accumulation in the large intestine
- Nature Downward Flowing
- Seat Abdomen, Base of Spine, Legs and Feet
- Physical Bones
- Aspect Moon, Feminine

---

[35] http://www.sanskritimagazine.com/ayurveda/secrets-marmas-vital-points-human-body/

111

Udana Vayu

This vayu of energy is outward moving in a spiral like a cartoon depiction of musical notes; it is responsible for speaking, singing, and all type of sounds like laughing, and crying etc.

A more subtle aspect of this type of prana is that it represents the conscious energy required to produce sound, the intention behind the words or noise.

Nature Upward Moving

Seat Marmas on Neck and Throat

Physical Muscles

Samana Vayu

- Responsible for inward movements of Prana such as digestion of food and cellular catabolism (break down and recycling of old cells) and thermo-regulation
- A visible source of the Samana current is the Aura; by meditating on Samana Vayu yogis can produce a lively aura
- Nature Inward Movements
- Seat Marmas of the Abdomen and Digestive Organs
- Physical Adipose Tissue (Fat)

Vyana Vayu

- Responsible for outward movements of Prana, extending the muscles and the pumping action of the blood vessels in the arteries
- Governs circulation and the skin
- This vayu represents the current that Reiki practitioners and hands on healers of all types use for energy medicine.
- Nature Outward Moving
- Seat Chest, Arm and Hand Marmas
- Physical Ligaments

Balancing Doshas in Reiki, Ayurveda and Massage

As energy healing practitioners we identify the Dosha, or constitution of the client. There are three Doshas in the body, consisting of the five elements. These doshas are Vata, Pitta and Kapha. We all have all three in varying proportions. Our primary balanced or Sattvic state of the balance of these five elements were in perfect balance upon birth. After birth we encounter imbalances and fluctuations which create an upsetting of our Sattvic state. In Ayurveda we are consistently working with the client to create and recreate this Sattvic balance. In Ayurvedic massage practitioners pay attention to the directions of energy and create balance with the movements upon the body. You can do this also by doing Marma massage. There are many online videos to show you how to do this, so we will table that discussion.

Balancing Doshas in Reiki, Ayurveda and Massage

The general idea is to balance the energies of the elements in the bodies back close to our Sattvic state in a gentle, holistic and sustainable way. We do this in Ayurveda with foods, herbal remedies, cleansing actions (kriyas), and many other ancient practices such as neti pot, nasya oil, dry brushing and Abayangha oil massage.

If there is too much Vata we Engage Apana and Prana, avoiding the energy movement of Udana, as this Vayu stirs up Vata (wind) in the upward moving nature, according to the list above.

If there is too much Pitta we engage Samana, assimilation, and Apana, downward flowing and grounding. We in turn avoid Udana, upward moving, and Vyana, outward moving.

If there is too much Kapha, earth and water energy, present we engage Udana to stir it upward and Vyana to move it out. In turn we avoid Samana and Apana, because Kaphic nature is already grounded and sometimes slow to move, and adding more Earth is going to upset that balance even further.

113

Once you understand the direction of the vayu flow you can engage that energy by performing massage strokes in the direction the vayu flows. For example, to engage Apana vayu stroke downward and outward on the body. We do this when we stroke along the colon across the body and then down. There are many types of Ayurvedic massage that is very helpful, one I highly recommend adding you your daily and weekly practice is partial and full Abayangha.

You can find your current dosha baby seeing an Ayurvedic specialist or to get an idea you can search an online quiz online.

What is Abhyanga?

Abhyanga is a beautiful form of massage, and self massage, in Ayurvedic medicine and timeless healing system. Ayurvedic massage has tremendous benefits to the mind, body, skin and immune system. Abhyanga may be done most commonly using oils with an herbal blend base oil and with essential oils customizable toward each person's dosha. This practice is a part of the Dinacharya, or the daily routine, suggested in your daily Sadhana practice.

The word 'abhyanga' is composed of two Sanskrit words, abhi and anga. Abhi means 'to rub' and anga, in one of its meanings, refers to 'limb' and together means 'loving hands'. Abhyanga is a synchronized massaging of the body towards the direction of the movement of arterial blood, and toward the heart. In practical terms it means massaging the body in the direction of the body hair. Abhyanga is considered a very important treatment modality for balancing the dosha Vata, and benefits all doshas to and cope with modern stresses, promoting longevity and nourishes virtually every part of the body.

Oils for Abyhanga

For Vata constitution, use sesame, olive or castor oil.

For Pitta constitution, use coconut, sunflower oil or ghee.

For Kapha constitution, use mustard, sesame, corn or olive oil.

For the body, use sesame, olive, sunflower, mustard or corn oils.

For the head, use coconut oil or sesame oil infused with cooling herbs.

For the feet use any oil appropriate for the dosha, or use ghee. [36]

The Three Bodies

*We are more than just our physical body. We are dynamic, whole, complex,
beautiful beings and we must honor all parts of ourselves if we want to
experience full joy, bliss, health, wellness, and balance. When someone
seriously devotes themselves to the practice, they bring all the parts of
themselves into alignment: mind, body, spirit.*
~Jenna Pacelli [37]

Affirmation: I am a soul incarnate manifest in a beautiful vessel. The yogi is very familiar with this concept. Yoga philosophy regards the body as the vehicle of the soul, as it travels on the journey toward enlightenment and refers to not just one body, but to three bodies, each being more subtle than the other.

The physical body is part of the food cycle and is experienced only in the waking state.

The astral body contains life energy, prana, as well as the senses and the mind. It is experienced in the waking and dream states.

The causal body is where happiness and joy are experienced in all three states of consciousness: waking, dreaming and deep sleep.[38]

The Five Koshas

Yoga facilitates the journey within to the deepest level of our being. According to ancient texts, every one of us have energetic layers or sheaths known as 'Koshas' that move from the periphery of the body towards the

---

[36] https://www.theayurvedaexperience.com/blog/ayurvedic-massage-abhyanga/
[37] https://peacefulvitality.wordpress.com/
[38] https://www.sivananda.eu/en/meditation/the-3-bodies.html

core of the self: the embodied soul. Each layer is an outcome of the energy it feeds on. Let's begin with the outermost layer, Annamaya kosha, this is made up of food; Pranamaya Kosha is made of Prana life force energy; Manomaya Kosha is formed with our thoughts; Vijanamaya Kosha is formed with the wisdom and knowledge and the last but most significant layer, Anandamaya Kosha is experienced as eternal bliss.[39] In the Upanishads the five sheaths (pancha-kosas) are described in the Taittiriya Upanishad.

The Five Koshas from physical to Astral:

1. Annamaya kosha, 'foodstuff' or physical sheath (Anna)

2. Pranamaya kosha, 'energy' sheath (Prana/apana)

3. Manomaya kosha 'mind-stuff' or emotional sheath (Manas)

4. Vijnanamaya kosha, 'wisdom' sheath (Vijnana)

5. Anandamaya kosha, 'bliss' sheath (Ananda)

According to Vedanta the wise person who is aware of the subtle influences of the five elements within each kosha, ever discerns the Self amidst appearances. Let's take a deeper study.

Annamaya kosha

This is the sheath of the physical self, named from the fact that it is nourished by food. Living through this layer man identifies himself with a mass of skin, flesh, fat, bones, and filth, while the man of discrimination knows his own self, the only reality that there is, as distinct from the body.

Pranamaya kosha

---

[39] https://fractalenlightenment.com/33744/spirituality/koshas-the-five-sheaths-that-wrap-your-soul

Pranamaya means composed of prana, the vital principle, the force that vitalizes and holds together the body and the mind. It pervades the whole organism; its one physical manifestation is the breath. As long as this vital principle exists in the organism, life continues. Coupled with the five organs of action it forms the vital sheath. In the Vivekachudamani it is a modification of vayu or air, it enters into and comes out of the body.

Manomaya kosha

Manomaya means composed of manas or mind. The mind (manas) along with the five sensory organs is said to constitute the manomaya kosa. The manomaya kosa, or "mind-sheath" is said more truly to approximate to personhood than annamaya kosa andpranamaya kosha. It is the cause of diversity, of I and Mine and Sanskrit likens it to clouds that are brought in by the wind and again driven away. Similarly, human's bondage is caused by the mind, and liberation, too.

Vijnanamaya kosha

This sheath is known also as the causal body. In deep sleep, when the mind and senses cease functioning, it still stands between the finite world and the self.

Anandamaya Kosha

Ananda maya means composed of ananda 'ahhhhh-nanda', or bliss. (Remember the ahh in asana, this is the same sound). Its the awareness of being whole and complete, exactly as you are. According to the Law of Attraction we are naturally like a cork, floating easily on the surface of the water. Our true happiness and joy is our natural state!

Anandamaya, or that which is composed of Supreme bliss, is regarded as the innermost of all. The bliss sheath normally has its fullest play during deep sleep: while in the dreaming and wakeful states, it has only a partial manifestation. It is the final layer standing between individual consciousness, self, and universal oneness Self. It is also seen as testimony of the love between Shiva and Shakti. This bliss state is usually experienced in fleeting moments in life, but can remain for longer periods. When we are fully present in the now moment we experience the Anandamaya Kosha, as well when in deep meditation. The blissful sheath is a reflection of the Truth, beauty, bliss and absolute.

In the Panchakosha discipline of yoga, each of the 5 Koshas represents a different aspect of the Higher Self.

Just as each of the five elements (earth, water, fire, air, and ether/space) appear in corresponding subtlety among each of the five senses, so does the intellect become ever subtler, and causes and effects become less dense through each of the five sheaths.[40]

For example, the Annamayakosha, the densest sheath, is based in the earth element. This is said to be guarded by Ganesha. The very subtlest sheath, closest to Spirit, Anandamaya, is based in the ether element, and is said to be guarded by a black disc of utter darkness over the sun, which can be removed only by Ganesha. The symbolism is very intriguing.

The Bhagavad Gita 3.40 states: The senses, the mind and the intelligence are the sitting places of this lust. Through them lust covers the real knowledge of the living entity and bewilders him.[41]

Awareness of the reflection of Highest Self within the most subtle sheath, Anandamayakosha, is the foundation for discernment of that which the elements, energies, senses, and kosha serve. With the awareness of all is created in service of the Highest Self for the Highest good, the components of the five Koshas can be helpful in daily meditation.

---

[40] http://www.yogawiz.com/yoga-therapy/the-five-sheaths.html
[41] http://vedabase.awardspace.com/bg/3/index.htm

118

Chapter 4 Feeding Your Chakras, What is Vinyasa Yoga

There are thousands of unknown elements in each food. Ten years ago we knew nothing about phyto-chemicals (phyto=plant, plant chemicals), but they were in whole foods, put there by nature, absorbed from the soil, and are absolutely necessary for normal metabolic activities. Without them we lay the foundation for a weak immune system and diseaseAs we journey through the chakras, we will check out the foods for each of the seven primary chakras to help determine where our current diets and lifestyles might be deficient or over-indulgent.[42] We can do our part in helping bring balance to our chakras by eating a balanced diet. We will discuss this in much greater detail in subsequent chapters. It may come as no surprise that the color of the chakras and the color of foods are inextricably linked. It is believed that eating a wide range of all the colors of the rainbow feed the chakras and all the organs.[43]

~Dr. Humbart 'Smoky' Santillo, Author of Your Body Speaks, Your Body Heals

Foods for the Chakras

Practicing clean eating and choosing all of the colors of the rainbow on our plate is one of the healthiest things we can do. To take a closer look at how food affects our energy system we will discuss each chakra and then add a theme, an affirmation and the list of recommended foods.

Feeding Your Root Chakra

Theme: Grounding

---

[42] http://healing.about.com/cs/chakras/a/learnchakras.htm
[43] http://www.smokeysantillo.com/juiceatricle.htm

119

Affirmation: I AM

- Root vegetables: carrots, potatoes, parsnips, radishes, beets, onions, garlic, etc.
- Protein-rich foods: eggs, clean meats, beans, tofu, soy products (non GMO), peanut butter, raw nuts
- Spices: horseradish, hot paprika, chives, cayenne, pepper
- Red foods: Red fruits and vegetables are great for balancing the root chakra. Strawberries, cherries, apples, pomegranates, tomatoes, beets and raspberries.[44]

Feeding Your Sacral Chakra

Theme: Nourishing, Divine Feminine, Sexuality, Creativity, Fertility

Affirmation: I FEEL

- Sweet fruits: melons, mangos, strawberries, passion fruit, oranges, coconut, etc.
- Honey (local)
- Raw Nuts: almonds, walnuts, sesame seeds, caraway seeds
- Spices: cinnamon, vanilla, carob, sweet paprika
- Coconuts: A hard encased fruit filled with a soft, white flesh and nourishing milk, the coconut embodies the feminine qualities of the sacral chakra. The fact that it is also full of good fats and oils make it perfect for this energetic vibration.
- Orange foods: Oranges, carrots, sweet potatoes, peaches, apricots, mangoes, papayas, pumpkin and mandarins, cuties, oranges are all sacral foods. When eaten with fats they help absorb more vitamins and mineral and they are excellent at restoring an unbalanced sacral chakra.

---

[44] http://jordannalevin.com/foods-that-balance-your-root-chakra/

Feeding Your Solar Plexus Chakra

Theme: Self Worth, Encouragement, Self Love

Affirmation: I DO

- Gluten free granola and Grains: pastas, breads, cereal, rices
- Flax seeds, sunflower seeds, foods high in healthy fats
- Clean organic dairy: non homogenized milk, hard cheeses, greek yogurt
- Spices and herbs: ginger, mints (peppermint, spearmint, etc.), Sweet Melissa, chamomile, turmeric, cumin, fennel
- Raw Cacao: dark chocolate helps with mental clarity and causes the body to release serotonin (the feel good hormone). The flavonoids in cacao have been shown to improve blood flow to the brain and the magnesium. Raw cacao helps to relieve stress and promotes relaxation.
- Purple foods: grapes, blackberries, blueberries, eggplants, purple kale, purple cabbage and purple grapes, purple sweet potatoes.
- Omega 3-rich foods: salmon, sardines, walnuts, flaxseeds and chia seeds all contain high levels of Omegas. Omegas from plants and clean, sustainable fish and non-harmful fishing practices are hard to come by. When eaten they are great for boosting brain power and balancing the third-eye chakra. I recommend the Omega Blend by Juice Plus+. It is sustainable and clean, all derived from 100% plant-based sources[45] to get in all these important Omega 3, 5, 6, 7, and 9's daily.

Feeding Your Heart Chakra

Theme: Healing, Emotional Connections

Affirmation: I LOVE

---

[45] www.juiceplus.com

- Green Leafy vegetables: spinach, kale, dandelion greens, etc.
- Air vegetables: Brussels sprouts, broccoli, cauliflower, green cabbage, celery, zucchini squash, peas and asparagus, Bok Choy
- Liquids: organic green teas, matcha tea, Yerba mate
- Green fruits: kiwi fruit, green apples, green grapes, cucumbers, avocado and limes.
- Green superfoods: spirulina, chlorella, wheatgrass, barley grass,
- Herbs: basil, sage, thyme, cilantro, parsley, coriander, mint, oregano, rosemary, tarragon

Feeding Your Throat Chakra

Theme: Speaking One's Truth, Faith

Affirmation: I SPEAK

- Liquids play a large role in healing the throat chakra because of their lubricating qualities; soups, warm teas, lots of pure water, fruit juices, herbal teas
- Avoiding dairy is highly recommended as it can congest your mucus membranes, coat the throat and clog the sinuses
- Blue foods: Blue is a color found rarely in natural foods. Blueberries, black grapes, blackberries
- Blended berries into a smoothie with hydrating coconut water to make a very healing throat chakra tonic
- Tree growing fruits: apples, pears, plums, peaches, apricots, mangoes, oranges and plums. They are 100% pure and ripe and chock full of phytonutrients when they are harvested after naturally falling off the tree
- Tart or tangy fruits: lemons, limes, grapefruit, kiwi, Meyer lemons
- Spices: salt, lemon grass

Feeding Your Brow Chakra

Theme: Awakening, Third Eye, Opening the 6th Sense, Pineal Gland

Affirmation: I SEE

Fasting is key to awakening when done with intention.

- Dark bluish colored fruits: blueberries, red grapes, black berries, raspberries, etc.
- Liquids: red wines and grape juice
- Spices: lavender when ingested, poppy seed, mugwort

Feeding Your Crown Chakra

Theme: Opening and Clearing, Spirituality, Higher Consciousness

Affirmation: I UNDERSTAND

- None of the five elements are associated therefore the most effective way to utilize the body to connect to Sahasrara is by fasting, cleansing, detoxing with intention
- Setting a Saklalpa: This means setting an intention formed by the heart and mind. It is a private and solemn vow and incorporates determination, commitment of a time period and strength of will. In practical terms a Sankalpa means a one-pointed resolve to focus both psychologically and philosophically on a specific goal. A sankalpa is a tool meant to harness the will, and to focus and harmonize mind and body[46].
- Incense and Smudging Herbs: White Mountain sage, copal, myrrh, frankincense, juniper, natural tobacco, Palo Santo, Amber
- Incense and smudging herbs are ritually inhaled through the nostrils or some can be smoked through a ceremony pipe for purification purposes. The resins are burned in a puja offering.

---

[46] wikipedia

123

- Open shaped sea shells are wonderful ceremonial tools for containing the puja offering of fire and incense. This also brings in the element of water to the ceremony.

In summary, this list is a great reference tool. When we know our goal is to balance out our systems and feed each of the chakras we must eat all the colors of the rainbow every single day. This task, as a rule, is our goal on this path of a Holistic Lifestyle. Even though we know what to do it is very difficult, as I am sure you may agree.

When I am working with my private coaching clients, as part of the process of discovery I have found that majority of people struggle in this area, no matter how much effort we do put forth. We simply do not get the 9 to 13 servings of fresh, organic, non-GMO fruits, veggies and berries we need every single day, nor do our children. Upon further exploration I find that many people are seeking answers to get in all these colorful foods. The solution I have found is a simple one. Eat closest to the Earth, grow your own food, and take Juice Plus whole food capsules or eat the Juice Plus chewables.

What is Vinyasa?

Vinyāsa pronounced 'vi-NYAAH-sa' is a Sanskrit term often employed in relation to certain styles of yoga. The term vinyasa may be broken down into its Sanskrit roots to assist in understanding its meaning.
Nyasa denotes "to place" and Vi denotes "in a special way." Like many Sanskrit words, vinyasa is a term that has many meanings.
Vinyasa is sequential movement that interlinks postures to form a continuous flow. It creates a moving meditation which reveals that all forms are impermanent. For this reason the poses are not held on to. Vinyasa is life,

movement, prana, breath, all integrated with alignment and perfect execution of the posture.[47]

There are four basic definitions of Vinyasa:

1) the linking of body movement with breath

2) a specific sequence of breath-synchronized movements used to transition between sustained postures

3) setting an intention for one's personal yoga practice and taking the necessary steps toward reaching that goal

4) a type of yoga class

Vinyasa denotes a flowing, dynamic form of yoga, connected to breath (mainly Ujayii pranayama) in which yoga and mudra transitions are embodied as links within and between each asana. Indeed, this process entrains the mind stream of consciousness with the body of the practitioner, and fuels the Samadhi. This by definition is the he higher level of concentrated meditation as discovered in the eight limbs of yoga. It is a Mystery in the adept; an affirmation that no value judgment between the importance or ascendancy of the asana or the transitions between asana is held. This view of non-judgement is grounded, founded and based in the Shunyata Doctrine which informed the development of vinyasa styles.[48]

Vinyasa Flow is also employed as a noun to describe the sequence of poses that are performed. In Intuitive Vinyasa we refer to this as the Low Flow or ½ Surya Namaskar, as we will discuss in detail in Chapter 7.

- Downward Facing Dog (Adho Mukha Svanasana),
- Plank (Plankasana),
- Four Limbed Staff Pose (Chatarangua),
- Upward Facing Dog (Urdhva Mukha Svanasana) to

---

[47] lisa ware 2015

[48] http://yoga.about.com/od/howtospeakyoga/g/asana.htm

- Downward Facing Dog (Adho Mukha Svanasana).

This is part of a Surya Namaskara, or Sun Salutation, sequence. This is more correctly termed half-vinyasa, as the full-vinyasa of Surya Namaskar returns to complete with standing asana in Tadasana (Mountain Pose) or Samasthiti (Starting Posture with Anjali Mudra). See the Complete Book of Vinyasa Yoga for the original Vinyasa sequences by Krishnamacharya, studied and integrated then written by Ramaswami.

Srivasta Ramaswami is a master teacher whom Lisa Ware has had the pleasure of studying with directly, author of The Complete Book of Vinyasa Yoga and a direct disciple of the legendary Yoga teacher Krishnamacharya, brings forth the essence of Vinyasa in asana practice in the following way, *"My guru believed that the correct vinyasa method is essential in order to receive the full benefits from yoga practice.*[49]*"*, states Ramaswami. The following statement perfectly captures this sentiment, *"From time immemorial the Vedic syllables...are chanted with the correct (high, low, and level) notes. Likewise, sruti (pitch) and laya (rhythm) govern Indian classical music. Classical Sanskrit poetry follows strict rules of chandas (meter), yati (caesura), and prasa (assemblage). Further, in mantra worship, nyasas (usually the assignment of different parts of the body to various deities, with mantras and gestures) ... are integral parts. Likewise yogasana (yogic poses), pranayama (yogic breathing exercises), and mudras (seals, locks, gestures) have been practiced with vinyasas from time immemorial. However, these days, in many places, many great souls who teach yoga do so without the vinyasas. They merely stretch or contract the limbs and proclaim that they are practicing yoga..."* as translated from Yoga Makaranda.

Ramaswami goes on to add, *"Just as music without proper pitch (sruti) and rhythm (laya) will not give happiness, yogasana practice without the*

---

[49] Srivasta Ramaswami, The Complete Book of Vinyasa Yoga

observance of vinyasas will not give health. That being the case what can I say about the long life, strength and other benefits?"

Vinyasa yoga, in which movement is synchronized to the breath, is a term that covers a broad range of yoga class styles. This style is sometimes also called 'Vinyasa Flow' yoga, because of the smooth way that the poses run together and become like a dance. The breath becomes an essential component because the teacher will guide the student with each and every breath. Throughout the entire practice the instructor is inviting students to move from one pose to the next on an inhale or an exhale. Vinyasa is literally translated from Sanskrit as meaning "connection," according to Ellen Stansell, PhD, RYT, a scholar of yogic literature and Sanskrit.

In terms of yoga asana (yogasana, as Ramaswami says) we can interpret this as a connection between movement and breath. In life, Vinyasa is the flow, the breath, the life force. Vinyasa is true beauty and art expressed in the form of the body. The perfection unlocks a connection to the Gurus and masters that came before us and brings. The Universe speaks in symbols and these asanas, bandhas and mudras are forms of energy, expressions of Prana, which brings us quickly into Divine communion when practiced with reverence and intention.

Krishnamacharya's Legacy

Krishnamacharya (1888-1989) was an Indian yogi and scholar. He claimed to have received his training in hatha yoga during seven years spent with his guru, Ramamohana Brahmacharya, who lived in a cave in a remote region of the Himalayas.

Krishnamacharya also spent many years studying, and then teaching Sanskrit, Vedic rituals, and philosophy. His approach to yoga is the first known to have incorporated movement through a series of poses coordinated with breathing, a style that is now known as vinyasa yoga. In his book Yoga

Body, Mark Singleton convincingly argues that the development of this flowing yoga was also heavily influenced by the physical culture movement of the 19th century and the gymnastic exercises practiced by members of the British military. In 1934, Krishnamacharya published Yoga Makaranda, a book covering the yoga methods and asanas he taught, many of which are familiar to yoga practitioners today.

From 1926 to 1946, Krishnamacharya ran a yoga school which actually was created mostly for young boys to offer the demonstration of the capacity of the human body.[50] It was strict and ruled with hard discipline; held at the palace of the Maharaja Krishnaraja Wodeyar in Mysore, India. During that time, Krishnamacharya had three prominent students who would go on to play pivotal roles in popularizing yoga in the west.

K. Pattabhi Jois was a devoted, long-time student whose vigorous Ashtanga style of asana was closely based on Krishnamacharya's teachings. Join thrived on the disciplines that his Guru enforced. He went on to create modern Ashtanga, and his account is one of the best windows we have into Krishnamacharya's yoga.

B.K.S. Iyengar, whose sister was Krishnamacharya's wife, received his first yoga instruction from his brother-in-law and was a student of the early teachings of his Guru before branching off to develop his own alignment-based style and bringing yoga to the west. The late B.K.S. Iyengar is one of the most influential yoga teachers in the world.

The Great Goddess of Yoga, Indra Devi

Indra Devi was a self made aristocrat, who was a life long seeker. She began her life as a woman of the stage and throughout her work she travelled incessantly. She greatly desired to find a guru. Indra Devi had a very interesting and influential life. When she first heard of Krishnamacharya she

---

[50] https://www.verywellfit.com/krishnamacharya-father-of-modern-yoga-3566898

found a way to be in his audience, as she was very good at creating opportunities and meeting people of great influence. She continued to come around the palace and into Krishmanacahrya's presence where he consistently ignored her. She became a regular in the palace he inadvertently became slightly entertained by her charm and charisma. Once the great teacher realized she was not going away, and she continued to ask him to, he then offered to teach her, on his terms, of course. She was Krishnamacharya's first female student. He gave her a bit of a different regime to practice, which was more attuned to a middle age woman, and not so much gymnastics. However greatly taxing, her practice was designed to test her discipline and her fortitude. She passed his approval and went on to bring yoga to the west, landing in California.

She was a globe trotter, before that was a thing! Indra Devi's story is a compelling account to the passions and purpose of a woman with the mission of spreading yoga, health, beauty and youth to the world. She is greatly responsible for the modern western feminine yoga movement, and this fame rose with her book, Forever Young Forever Healthy. She became a yoga teacher to the upper class housewives and the Hollywood starlets in the 1940s and 50s, going on to teach and lecture world wide. She died at 103, still working up to the very end! She is a great inspiration for all women. Her biography is highly recommended, The Goddess Pose by Michelle Goldberg.

Yoga Teaching Tips Signature Vinyasa 101 Class

In the signature style, Yoga 4 Love's Intuitive Vinyasa yoga, we label the classes to help students know what they are enrolling in and to be descriptive of a little bit of what to expect.

Yoga 101 is a beginner, all levels and mixed levels practice. It can be taught hot, 95-100 degrees Fahrenheit or temperate at 80 degrees. Many options are to be creative here when you are ready to design your own sequence. For more on this topic we will discuss and give you the entire Beginner Yoga 5 Week Series in Chapter 7. One important teaching to begin with in a workshop is to explain Vinyasa. How do we begin to teach students what vinyasa is? To begin, simply explain that it means to place in a specific order. We link our breath to our movement.

In a workshop setting we have opportunity to break down certain elements of a yoga class. The definition of Hatha Yoga is as follows: Ha-Sun, Surya; Tha moon, Chandra; hatha together means 'Forceful.

As good yoga teachers we use cues to guide the class. Staying in the positive present tense, use inclusive language (our vs your), using many adverbs and adjectives.

Here are some intentions to sprinkle in as cues to get you started.

We are...

- o   Remembering that our breath is our foundation for yoga.
- o   Creating space for ourself
- o   Listening to our bodies.
- o   Ensuring that our breathing practice is intentional.
- o   Doing yoga no matter what the pose looks like or what pose we are in.
- o   As long as we are focusing on our breath we are doing yoga.
- o   Keeping our minds on our mats.
- o   Honoring our bodies.
- o   Letting go (...of our day, our past weekend, our past year; of what the rest of the class is doing; of to do lists, our inbox; or what it took to get to class.)
- o   Breathing.
- o   Let go of competition within.

- o Feeling. [51]

- o Checking in and staying in the present moment.

- o Keeping our focus. finding our Drishti, our focal point.

- o Focusing on own practice, our own breath, letting go of anything going on around us.

- o Letting go of any sense of judgment of ourselves or others.

Beginner 101 Teaching Tips

In any Beginner 101 class we have opportunity to teach Vinyasa sequenced with a Y4L Signature Beginner yoga class. This is a basic format for that class or practice:

Introduce basic Pranayama at the beginning of each class such as 3 Part Breathing, Alternate Nostril Breathing, Ujayii Breath

It is also important to our Y4L signature style of yoga to demo the postures first then you may also choose to walk, adjust and teach. When in a workshop it is a good idea to have demo models so you can break down the flow.

- Demo for the class while you teach if you are in a flow class, or have a demo model.

- Keep the prana up with your own enthusiasm, positivity and encouraging energy.

- Use your voice and inflection to guide the class:

- Increase volume and excitement to signal to push harder and keep the energy up to increase Prana.

- Decrease volume and meter to indicate when to bring it down.

- Intentionally increase volume above normal speaking tone intentionally when: demoing, inverted, facing the back, face near the earth, twisting etc.

---

[51] YogaFit.com

- Offer cues for taking resting postures as options throughout the flow.

- Offer opportunities to find their edge and encourage them to do so while listening to their body.

Yoga Class Etiquette, What to Do and What to Avoid

Here is a list of do's and a list of what to avoid, in which I have compromised over the last decade of teaching.

What to Do:

Arrive a bit early to sign in and to sit on your mat. Getting to class a few minutes early can help you settle in and align your attitude with the purpose of the class. While you're waiting you can practice a pose, stretch, or meditate quietly, breathe, and get centered. In a Far Infrared heated studio, it is nice to sit and relax.

Let your teacher know about any injuries or conditions that might affect your practice[52]. If you are injured or have a limitation, skip poses you can't or shouldn't do, or try a modified version even if the rest of the class is doing something else. Please make note to speak to each new teacher of your injuries or limitation.

Set your intention. An important part of our practice is finding our focus our drishdi. Some find it helpful to dedicate your practice to a certain intention, gratitude or something higher than ourselves. Find our intention to be loving, kind and compassionate, or healthier, stronger or more powerful. You may dedicate your yoga practice to ones who cannot practice, to a friend, a cause or your Higher Self.

Take time reflect and meditate This helps us retain what you practiced and extend the sense of bliss we achieve on our mat with a strong asana flow.

---

[52] Tim Noworytas yogajournal.com

Review the poses you practiced, note any cues that made sense and came up for you. Even if you remember just one thing from each class, you'll soon have a lot of information that you can pull from in times of need. Through your own perseverance on the mat you will find that you are able to use this applied yogic knowledge off the mat. This practice will help you persevere tough situations in everyday life.

Please be quiet It's great to share a class with a friend, but it is very distracting to yourself and others to have a conversation or be giggly in the back of the studio.

Keep your focal point and your mind and on your mat. It is difficult at first to not have to look around to see how to do a pose. Begin to trust the audio cues from the instructor, and trust your own feeling in your body to see if the pose feels good for you. Find your focal point and try not to look in the mirror (if you have one) or around the class too much. Yoga is as much about an internal focus, a moving meditation, as well as a physical practice. After a few short weeks you will be surprised at the changes you already have observed in your body, mind and spirit.

Bring your own hand towel or your own mat, especially if you sweat.

Put away any props or mats that you use, neatly the way you found them. Clean any borrowed mats or props thoroughly.

What to avoid:

Avoid wearing heavy fragrances, strong herbal muscle relaxer, perfume or slippery lotions before practice. Arrive clean and free of scents that might distract, offend or make others feel nauseated. Many people are highly sensitive to perfumes, and chemical scents are much stronger especially when sweaty.

Avoid eating for one or three hours before class, depending on your metabolism and the intensity of your upcoming practice. If you practice yoga before your food has passed through your stomach you might experience cramps. If you have a full belly you are likely to experience nausea, or vomiting, especially in twists, deep forward bends, and inversions. Digesting food also takes energy that can make you lethargic. Hot classes are much more likely to bring this to the surface.

Avoid bringing cell phones into class. Leave your phone for the practice. Seriously, you will be fine without your phone. Do not bring your phone to your mat, turn on silent or best, place on Airplane mode. (this is a great practice to do every night!)

Avoid any business calls or using your cell until your practice is complete and you have left the studio space, so the peace of the practice space is not disturbed. If you have a reason to keep your phone by you for emergency, please let the instructor know and place it in an inconspicuous place near you, on silent or under a towel. If you must respond to your phone please do so in the restroom or the lobby, NEVER on your mat.

Remove all electronic devices from your body, Apple Watches, FitBit, etc. Your practice time is sacred! These devices are strong enough to communicate with a satellite so they are giving off EMTs and affecting your energy field. You may log your practice on your app later.

Be aware of going too fast, too far past your edge too soon. Instead of trying to go as deeply or completely into a pose as others might be able to do, do what you can without straining or injuring yourself. You'll go farther faster if you take a loving attitude of Metta toward yourself and work from where you are with your breath. Avoid doing a pose from the intention of where you think you should be or the outcome.

Avoid coming into class late. If you must do this, please let the instructor know before the practice begins, so that they may place a mat for you in a proper place near the door; and make this a once in a blue moon occurrence not a habit. Coming in late is disruptive to others. People are curious and will feel the need to look at you and the door opening so if you are late, try to come in like a cat and be as inconspicuous as possible. Avoid loud noises rolling out your mat. If you come in late or leave early more than once or twice please consider the disruption you are causing and take a different class at a more convenient time.

Especially avoid leaving early before Savasana (final relaxation); this is considered very poor yoga etiquette and actually really rude. Savasana is part of your practice; you earned it and is your reward for a wonderful class. Many physiological and psychological benefits are documented with a nice Savasana. Turn off your mind and to do list and be in the NOW. Enjoy it!

What Is Yoga and How Can I Benefit From It?

Yoga is one of the oldest forms of movement in history, although the asana practice began many, many years after the beginning of yoga. The connection between the Ancient Yogis and the modern day Western yoga practitioner today are still evident, although subtle. Yoga is composed of linking together poses, the body's energy and the breath[53]. There are many benefits of yoga such as:

- Learning to quiet the chatter in the mind.

- Building bone density; weight bearing exercise is actually the only way to do this, not weight lifting.

- Listening and becoming more in tune with your body, mind and Spirit.

- Creating a place for 'me time' on calendar and on your yoga mat.

- Building strength, core power, agility, grace and endurance.

---

[53] http://www.examiner.com/article/what-is-yoga-and-how-can-i-benefit-from-it

- Bringing a greater awareness of the interconnection of ourselves and nature.

- Building a stronger connection to Spirituality.

- Increasing flexibility, no matter how inflexible one is to start. It is a common misconception that one must be flexible to begin yoga. The only condition to begin yoga is an intention.

- Decreasing stress levels, knots, tension and Cortizol dramatically by increasing release of the anti stress hormones DHEA and Oxytocin through a regular yoga practice.

- Increasing your daily energy level.

- Increasing your libido. (Yep, you read that one right!)

- Developing healthy lifestyle habits.

- Surrounding yourself with people who lift you up.

- Making new acquaintances and friends in the community.

- Becoming interconnected in the worldwide movement of positive, conscious, like minded individuals.

Finding a Yoga Studio or Class That's a Fit

Professional yoga teachers are taught through many lineages. To become a Registered Yoga Teacher, RYT it requires at least 200 hours of training and many practice and internship hours. All schools are required to teach a variety of yoga asana and history in the curriculum. Finding a yoga studio or class that fits you may not be the first one you step into. Some yoga studios teach only the poses, or asanas, which is strictly the movement. Some yoga styles teach just the asana similar to a bootcamp, some only the breath and the movement. Others focus on the entire mind, body, spirit connection.

Yoga is a practice unlike any other movement, sport or art in the world. Some people may associate yoga with a particular religion. This is untrue and not even possible as a whole, for each person is vastly different from the next. Each person brings to their mat their own belief system. Yoga is what each individual interprets it to be, therefore, each individual's yoga practice experience is vastly varied from another's. Each person will walk off their mat into the world with the tools and inner dialogue that suits exactly what they need that day, on the condition that they let go and are open to the possibilities of what their body, breath and mind have for them in that present moment.

Staying in the present moment, guided gently to push to the edge, leading into a blissful state of final relaxation; this is yoga. Yoga is a wonderful addition to any lifestyle.[54]

Yoga 4 Love's Basic Beginner Yoga Terms

Listed below are common terms that are most frequently used, and their basic meanings.

Asana- (pronounced: AHH-sa-na) Poses, postures, positions used in the physical practice of Yoga, one of the 8 limbs of yoga; one of the 8 Limbs of Yoga.[55]

Bandhas- Yogic locks utilized in poses and breathwork to restore maintain and build the natural energy level in the body, mind and perhaps connection to spirit; utilized to direct your prana.

---

[54] Lisa Ware, circa 2012
[55] Answers.com

Gentle Heat- The room is not air conditioned nor hot and kept around 82- 87. This is a comfortable temperature for yoga practice, ideal for beginners, baby boomers, pre and post natal, teens and kids.

Hatha Yoga- This is an ancient practice of yoga and one of the most popular utilizing asana, pranayama , meditation and Savasana to achieve better health, wellness and instill an inner calm or focus.

Gentle Heated Yoga- Yoga practiced in a warm room, temperature 87 - 89 degrees, to get the muscles ready for movement. Practicing in a warm room helps to prevent injury.

Hot Yoga- Yoga practiced in a room 95 to 105 degrees. The heat allows the detox the body, focus the mind and clarify the cardiovascular system. Some practices add 65- 80% humidity; this intensifies the detox and sweat. Take several classes to let the body and mind acclimate to the heat, drink plenty of water, and rest when needed. Far Infrared Heat, Space Heat, Central heat or Coals with steam are options to heat the space. All types have different effects and benefits or detractions. To clarify a common misconception, Bikram Yoga is not the same as Hot Yoga. The aforementioned brand is just that, a brand that is a specific style of a 26 sequenced yoga practice, and not referring to a general hot studio.

OM- The supreme and most sacred syllable, consisting in Sanskrit of the three sounds (a), (u), and (m), representing various fundamental triads and believed to be the spoken essence of the universe. It is uttered as a mantra and in affirmations and blessings. It can be spelled in Sanskrit 'om' or 'aum'.

Pranayama- Breathing intentionally breath work and breath awareness; essential in the connection of mind/body, one of the 8 Limbs of Yoga.

Reiki- Reiki is a healing therapy focusing on the body's basic energies, guided by a certified and attuned Reiki Practitioner or Reiki Master. Reiki utilizes gentle hand positions and relaxation with guided imagery. The recipient is safe, protected and loved as blockages in their energy or physical body are released. Rei = Universal/ Ki = energy, life force, prana.

Prana- The body's natural energy; sometimes referred to Chi or Ki. Life force.

Savasana- Final relaxation, corpse pose. This pose completes all traditional yoga practices and is an important part of the class.

Thai Yoga Massage/ Thai Bodywork- This is applied yoga, a combination of a massage session and a yoga practice, where the recipient is fully relaxed and the practitioner moves the client through a full range of motion, utilizing acupressure points and the energy lines in the body, the client leaves feeling refreshed and energized.

Vinyasa Flow- Yoga postures placed in a meaningful sequence with breath. A form of Hatha Yoga. This yoga is Breath Synchronized Movement, meditation in motion. Each inhale and exhale has an associated movement, the space between movements are intentional, as well. Postures are sequenced purposefully and placed in a specific order.

Yoga Practice- a 'yoga practice' has a much different intention than a 'workout'. Vinyasa is an art form, it is the art and science of moving through the asanas and breathing techniques to achieve calmness of mind, balance of body and connection to spirit. The styles and intensity are varied wide and far.

Yoga 101- Yoga 4 Love branding for Yoga for beginner levels and/or a relaxing class. This is a Vinyasa or Hatha practice with some a lot of props and verbally cued modifications.

Yoga 201- This is a brand of Yoga 4 Love for mixed level and all levels focusing on a solar standing series that is a strong Vinyasa flow with one or two peak poses, some core building heat then a wonderful final relaxation.

Yoga 301- The 301 class is a brand of Yoga 4 Love classes that are focused on teaching intermediate or advanced students, or adventurous beginners.[56] This class embodies the flow of Intuitive Vinyasa, with three to four standing solar flows, two to three peak postures and overall bringing students to find their personal edge on the mat.

---

[56] This term 'Adventurous Beginner' came from Ricky Tran, an amazing yoga teacher and good friend of Lisa's

Chapter 5 Mindfulness, Moon Cycles, Rhythms and Holistic Living

Everything is energy and that's all there is. Match the frequency of the reality

you want and you cannot help but get that reality. It can be no other way.

This is not philosophy. This is physics

~Albert Einstein

Intro to Mindfulness + Holistic Living

Join me for our next step in the journey as we delve into Mindfulness and Holistic Living! Be my guest as I bring you to a path leading to less stress and a healthy lifestyle. We will learn many applicable tools. I have developed these along on my life long journey by being out in nature, using simplified plant based nutrition and clean eating; practicing yoga, doing energy work and through meditation.

In these chapters we incorporate a daily practice of holistic living tools, quiet time and mindfulness. You can utilize these tools while preparing food, meditating and in yoga, as well as in the everyday moments in all your roles of daily life. Whether you are a mom, dad, pet owner, daughter, co-worker, entrepreneur or wife you will gain basic ways for slowing down, relieving stress, managing your energy and your calendar and ultimately your choices. Many of these chapters have additional resources, journaling exercises and handouts on our website www.yoga4love.com. You may have an intention to become more intentional in mindful living, or this may be totally new! Wherever you are in this NOW moment, going forward, together, by accessing these lifecoaching tips you will move closer to creating the perfect space for what you love and how to have more joy in your life!

Baby steps are all you need to take steps toward leaning into your aligned sacred path. Daily application is the most important, and taking time upfront to go within to create your intention. Through small, simple steps you will be headed on the path of what your heart desires and step into, or further, your personal journey toward health, happiness and success via a holistic lifestyle.

Divine Love Keys, Affirmations + Steps to Abundance

A successful life depends on a foundation of belief. Truly believing and being in gratitude of the blessings we are yet to receive is the KEY to manifesting abundance! This is a Native American Proverb and a great way to live our life; Self-trust, Self-love and Self-belief. The Universe is patiently waiting and conspiring to give you your heart's desires. ALL OF THEM!

When you give yourself the permission to completely accept yourself and your blessings, you are saying to the Universe, "I am ready to receive!" BRING ON THE ABUNDANCE!

- Today, I let life flow through my experience, bringing new events to pass.
- Today, I let go of the old and let the new appear.
- Today, my entire being is open and ready to receive all good.
- Today, I am an expression of Divine Love.

Steps to creating mindfulness in receiving abundance are a simple process, and it becomes easier to do once it becomes a habit. First state your outcome in the positive; what specifically do you want? Specify your present situation and get connected within; where am I now? Then ask; where do I want to be?

Clarify your outcome by using all of your senses, as if you already have it, in the positive present tense. When I receive this blessing how does it look? How does it sound? How does it feel (taste or smell) now that I have

142

it? Specify your evidence procedure, being totally clear on what you are intending. This is so that when you receive it you are clearly aware of exactly when your blessings arrive! Ask; how will I know when I have received my blessing(s)?

Design the journey to the outcome to be desirable and fun! Identify the outcome in many descriptive ways so it will increase your choices.What will this blessing allow myself to do, be, see? Ensure that it the outcome is self initiated and self maintained and not dependent on others.

Next, ask how can I start the steps toward my goal? What does it take to maintain the achievement of this goal? Put every step in context to get a clearer overall picture of exactly what you are manifesting in your life.

Ask these questions; where, when, how and with whom do I want it? Writing these leading questions in a journal and coming back to them often. Use this simple process whenever you are asking the Universe (Source) for blessings. Make a notebook to refer to, write what and when you ask and also notate when you receive! As this practice becomes a daily behavior you will also begin to notice the time between asking and receiving is getting shorter and shorter![57] This is a really fun way to live!

There are so many examples of this in my life, and too many to start naming. Let's just suffice it to say, it works!!!

Start Where I AM Now! Tapping into the Rhythms of Nature

Here are some tools to enlighten you about where you are right now. Some call this intuition; however we all already have this. It is not a sixth sense, but an inner awareness, a practice of not DELETING what is right before our very eyes. Women already seem to sense these things on some level, but going through the formal process brings this inner knowing to a more tangible level.

---

[57] For more on asking the Universe watch the movie 'The Secret'

First, let's turn our attention to what's already happening with nature and our moods. Moods seem to change with the seasons. Our moods mirror inside of us what's happening outside and in the Earth, the moon, the sun and the planets.

We are all energetic beings! We are simply energy contained in a seemingly dense container or vessel. We are each vibrating at a level that keeps us on this planet, thanks to gravity and the Laws of Physics. In less than 12 months all of our cells will have turned over and are not the same. We think we are mass, but can we all agree that everything is all energy, including us?

I am a huge moon goddess, and by watching the cycles of the moon, the equinoxes, the solstices and the Celtic seasonal calendar I can determine when my own moon cycle will start. By being aware of the moon cycle, then journaling, you will soon learn if that's true for you, too.

Weekly Energy, Mood, Moon and Season Journaling

This is a great way to tap in to your own cycles and learn about how you are affected. Here are a few prompts to get you started: Where is the cycle of the moon this week (new, waxing, full, waning). What is going on with the solar system (Mercury retrograde, solar flares, astrological charts). What is the weather in my ares like each day? What is my mood/energy upon waking; my mood/energy upon retiring?

At the end of the month please journal about your overall mood. Note your theme and things you noticed in these patterns that have emerged.

Goddess Moon Cycle and the Celtic Calendar

Celtic tradition and culture honored the wisdom of the earth. Women were honored as healers and midwives. The cycles of the Sun and Moon were honored as well. The Celts learned about the power of the plants and trees to heal. They prayed to the elements, the animals, the trees and the rocks. All held essence and spirit and teaching. Reverence and gratitude were part and

parcel of everyday life. Contact with unseen worlds was taken for granted, and magic was developed out of knowledge given through communication with other dimensions. Shamanism was not out of the ordinary.
~Sharlyn Hidalgo, The Healing Power of Trees

By learning from the indigenous teachings, by tuning into the season, the time of the year and the time of the day we can learn so much about ourselves. The annual Celtic calendar consists of the 13 moons of the year. Each moon phase has an exact date range, a tree and a God, Elemental or Goddess archetype representing the energy of that tree and that time of year.[58] These cycles have been honored for thousands of years. Like the moon calendar, we, as humans or 'two-leggeds', all have an internal clock. This clock is regulated by our connections to the elements within our bodies, the sunrise, the sunset and the planets. These cycles are referred to as our circadian rhythm. It can also be deregulated inadvertently by lack of self care and disconnect from these energies and Universal rhythms. In addition, according to our Native American teachings we all each have our 'Hour of Power. This is the time during the day when we are naturally, totally and completely in the flow.

In Ayurveda we follow a 24 hour clock for eating. We eat our biggest meal when the sun is at the zenith or there is the most prana present. Many practices also follow the moon cycle, and fast from grains or eat less grains, on the 11th day following the new and full moon cycle, according to the days with the least prana, or energy.[59]

We are all energetic beings! We are simply energy contained in a seemingly dense container or vessel. We are each vibrating at a level that keeps us on this planet, thanks to gravity and the Laws of Physics. In less

---

[58] The Healing Power of Trees by Sharlyn Hidalgo
[59] The 11th day is a practice of the Hare Krishna movement

than 12 months almost all of our cells will have turned over anew and are not the same. We think we are mass, but can we all agree that everything is all energy, including us?

Here are some tools to enlighten you about where you are right now. Some call this intuition, however we all already have this. It is not a sixth sense, but an inner awareness, a practice of not deleting what is right before our very eyes. Most women already seem to sense these things on some level, but by going through the formal process, we bring this inner knowing to a more tangible level.

To begin, let's turn our attention to what's already happening with nature and our moods. Moods seem to change with the seasons. Our moods mirror inside of us what's happening outside and in the Earth, the moon, the sun and the planets.

As women, or goddesses, we are very in tune with the moon, as our lunar ebb and flow governs our female monthly moon cycle, birth and even for many, death. The new and full moon are a time when as a creative and writer I get my most energy and brilliant ideas! I can literally feel the moon energy rising, because the ideas and material I produce downloads so fast. Manifestations happen quickly during these lunar times.

Mood, Actions, Food and Nutrition Journaling Exercise
For the next week jot down how you feel, what your general mood is like, during these times: Sunrise, Waking, Mid-Morning, Noon, Mid-Afternoon, Evening/Sunset, Night. Make sure to take time to look at the cycle and see the patterns emerge. For ladies it is important to also mark your menstrual cycle, your ovulation and your phantom cycle, if in peri or menopause.

Next, for a week take a journal with you or make a commitment to simply write in these things at the end of the day for at least seven days.[60] Jot down everything you put into your body that day. I find it is easiest to do this as I go, because I am a 'Do It NOW' kinda goddess, and I also forget what I eat by the next day and can spend too much time trying to recall everything! A great tool for tracking that one of my teacher trainees once shared with me is the free 'My Fitness Pal' app.[61] To begin, use the app or jot down these categories and make a chart for the week: Breakfast, Snack, Lunch, Snack, Dinner. Then, track your food, water, supplements and literally anything that goes in to your mouth for a week.

Now, make a checklist chart for the each day of the week for these daily activities: Movement, Spiritual Connection, Prayer and Quiet Time, Meditation, Daily Sadhana. No need to go into detail, just check it off if/when you did these things that day.

Lastly make a check list for these relationships, and intend for the important ones to be nurtured for sure each week: Self Care/Spirituality, Friends, Immediate Family, Life Partner/Spouse, Kids, Community Outreach/Charity, Fun/Recreation.

After your week of journaling answer this last two questions: what patterns have I noticed? What are the three things that influence my mood the most?

By setting your intention and taking the time for your own self discovery you will quickly be on the high road to true Holistic Health, mindfulness, healing and longevity!

---

[60] PositivelySunny.net
[61] My Fitness Pal is trademarked by Under Armor

Chapter 6 Your Secret Sauce; Joy! Less Stress, More Success

Sometimes your JOY is the source of your smile, but sometimes your smile
can be the source of your JOY.
~Thich Nhat Hanh

What is your special sauce? Does your cup runner over with Joy?

Is it time to put more thought into your special 'Secret Sauce'. So, think about what brings you your own personal brand of Joy? Well, it is those very things you answered, that become your very own Special Secret Sauce.

In our Western culture we tend to deny ourselves many joys. The old belief is that we must sacrifice to be happy and joyful. This is the farthest from Truth. Did you realize that both excitement and fear feel the same way? They both feel just like butterflies in the stomach! Joy is a choice! You can choose! Believe! Live your life in Faith not fear! It is time to choose Joy!

Which Wolf Do You Feed?

One evening an elder Cherokee told his grandson about a battle that goes on inside all people. He said, "My son, the battle is between two wolves inside us. One is Fear. It carries anxiety, concern, uncertainty, hesitancy, indecision and inaction. The other is Faith. It brings calm, conviction, confidence, enthusiasm, decisiveness, excitement and action." The grandson thought about it for a moment and then meekly asked his grandfather: "Which wolf wins?" The old Cherokee replied, "The one you feed." Your journey toward extraordinary results will be built above all else on faith. It's only when you have faith in your purpose and priorities that you'll seek out

148

your ONE Thing. And once certain you know it, you'll have the personal power necessary to push you through any hesitancy to do it. Faith ultimately leads to action, and when we take action we avoid the very thing that could undermine or undo everything we've worked for—regret." ~Gary Keller, Author, The ONE Thing[62]

Finding Your Secret Sauce Exercise + Affirmations

Let's begin with some self reflection. Ask yourself these questions. See what you may uncover within that will propel you in the direction of filling finding your Secret Sauce!

What one thing can you do RIGHT NOW, immediately, to take yourself to a place of inner joy?[63]

Do you have a memory that uplifts you as soon as you feel, taste and see it?

Is there an aroma of which propels you to a joyful time at the hint of a whiff?

When was the last time you laughed and cried (maybe peed) at the same time because something was so happy, joyful and funny all at the same time?

Imagine when you pick up or hug an animal such as your favorite a dog or cat or a hug or pet a horse. Describe what you feel like you are full in this place of love and joy?

Bring picture into your mind of a person, place, experience, etc that warms your heart with joy every time you see or think of it. Write many of these triggers down in your journal. Continue to add more mindful habits to the new Joy filled Spirit led life you are consciously creating!

---

[62] Gary Keller, The ONE Thing: The Surprisingly Simple Truth Behind Extraordinary Results
[63] www.lessstressmorejoy.com

Finish these sentences with what is appropriate for you today, right now:

- I define joy for me as:
- My greatest joy is:
- I experience a sense of joy every time I :
- What gets in my way of doing something that would bring me joy?
- The last three times I was feeling truly joyful were:
- When I am truly joyful by body and mind feel:
- I will create more joy right now and the first thing I will do is:
- When I was a kid, I use to...and that was my secret sauce.
- This is what real joy to me as an adult:
- I AM committed to being more mindful and adding more joy to my life by taking this action:
- Do I have actually space in my life for my 'Secret Sauce'?
- What actions am I taking today to begin to remove some stressors?
-

Secret Sauce Affirmations

- I NOW commit to allowing more Joy and creating more mindfulness in my daily life.
- I AM stepping into clarity and walking in my Power.
- I AM activating my Secret Sauce by taking positive actions.
- I AM a beautiful child of Creator.
- I NOW claim my birthright for an AMAZING joyful life, filled with my Secret Sauce!

And it is so! Aho!

Namaste.

Yoga is a practical and enjoyable way to attain balance in your body, peace in your mind and focus for your Spirit. The physical practice of yoga offers so many variations for everyone's different needs. Yoga can be very physically active, depending on the style.[64] Following are the fundamentals to living a happy, healthy and fit lifestyle.

• Get enough rest: 7.5 - 8.5 hours is ideal for most people.

• Eat foods that are colorful; 'Eat the Rainbow' and avoid too many soft or sticky foods. Eat 4-7 small meals/ large snacks a day, avoiding heavy large meals which tend to bog down your energy level and take time to digest.

• Eat foods that you can identify their source; where did the ingredients come from? The closer to the Earth, the better for you as a general rule. Look for and go out of your way to make sustainable choices, do it for your grandchildren's children.

• Drink pure water, half an ounce per pound of body weight daily is recommended. If what you're drinking isn't just water, drink 100% juice, organic or non dairy milk, caffeine free and free from artificial color and fake sweeteners. Keep a travel bottle with you at all times. Americans are almost always within 25 feet of a water source and most go around dehydrated every day! Avoid soft drinks entirely, yes, even the clear ones. Your body's pH levels immediately turn very acidic and stay that way until you drink about 30 glasses of pure water to counter that one soft drink. All dis-ease develops in an acidic environment.

• Avoid wasting time and energy running around. Prepare your week in advance. Plan major tasks for each role in your life and write them down.

---

[64] original article by Lisa Ware printed in 2011 Dallas Yoga Examiner

Be open to change, and add time in for changes, as change is truly the only constant in our life.

- Set realistic goals, make lists. Set your aim high and shoot for the moon. Even if you miss you will land among the stars![65]

- Do something every day to connect to a higher source or a bigger cause, however that connection relates to you most. Whether it translates to giving time or resources for charitable works, setting your intention in prayer, meditation, in nature or sitting in quiet time; make this a daily commitment to yourself.

- Allocate time for special friends and family. Keeping those relationships nurtured and caring about others makes you feel better and is want really helps us through the hard times. When life is stripped to the basics these are the people that matter most.

- Demonstrate random acts of kindness.

- Learn something new! Set things to look forward to this week, this month and this year. Read, study, travel, spend time doing things you simply enjoy. That may be spending time at the barn or a day crafting or creating artwork… whatever lights you up!

- Be good to your body. Do a physical activity daily! Sweat, focus, and get your heart rate up, change it up to keep it interesting, but most importantly HAVE FUN doing it! Yoga is a great way to achieve balance, relieve stress and gain awareness and focus, all in one hour on your yoga mat a few times a week! After learning techniques on your yoga mat in class, you will develop new skills to utilize in real life off your mat. As we push ourselves physically in class, we also take what we learn and translate that to pushing

---

[65] adapted from a quote from Mary Kay Ash

through any hard situation in life. You may quickly experience better inner awareness, less reaction and more pro-action.

• Learning to breathe! This may sound automatic, but not breathing fully is a stress reaction and can be a symptom, or even a cause, of many dis-eases, plus getting more oxygen is always a lovely benefit.

Healthy living and doing yoga go hand in hand. As we grow and practice in yoga, we develop our character and learn to take that very important time to disconnect from stimulus, technology and the constant bombardment of our senses. This is called OVERSTIMULATION; we can learn to live in peace in a chaotic world. We instead turn to find a moment for ourselves, away from our regular routine. Just a simple hour on our yoga mats or in nature. We then in turn help nurture our relationships through loving kindness with others and to ourselves, as we practice yoga without forcing our bodies and learning to observe rather than always press on. Yoga ultimately helps us respond with love by using our practice as a mirror. We see our self from a new perspective, developing discipline. This yoga is about developing character, learning to find stillness, getting stronger, more balanced and, of course, more flexible, in both body and mind.

By each of us committing to have a positive outlook and by utilizing these learned skills on our mat in real life off our mat, we will be contributing our small part to making our community, and ultimately our planet, a better place to live!

Cutting Energetic Ties, Reiki and Shamanic Practitioner Work

With whom are you holding onto past resentments or grievances that no longer serve you?[66] With whom do you need to cut the energetic ties in order to reconnect a new? Where are you most stuck in your life? Why are

---

[66] Touchstone for Life by Gary Quinn

you stuck? Who do you need to forgive? Remember forgiveness is not for them, it is for your SELF.

To cut energetic ties from someone or something the first step is to intend to bring back all your power. This comes from the Shamanic Practitioner work and we call this Stalking Your Power.[67]

Reiki energy is a super helpful tool to use. If that is not yet in your tool belt you may look up a Reiki practitioner to help guide you and even book a session. If you don't know where to start please find either a Shamanic Practitioner or Reiki Master in your area from a referral or on a credible resource online.

For this exercise in cutting off our energetic ties, it is really simple. In this process we must first get into meditation and deep relaxation. To begin, set your intention. Then ask for help from your Source, Master Teachers, Guides, Angels, Archangels, Spirit and Power Animals and Ancestors. You are totally and completely protected when working in the Light of Christ Consciousness. Surround your energy field with protection of Christ and the Archangels.

You may do this work with a partner or alone. Call in your energy and your power. Demand it return to you, its rightful owner, from all time, past, present and future. Ask that all power is returned to you from wherever it was given or taken away. It could have been given by you or taken by anyone or from anywhere, this doesn't matter. Simply call in your Power!!! Feel it returning, and feel the wholeness. Relax and breathe.

Now, ask to release any energy that is not yours to return to its original source, and anything that is not of the Light. See it drain away easily, just like rain water. This is a relaxing and releasing process. Send it off with love and light and feel gratitude for its lessons. Let go of the emotions and keep the wisdom. Thank it and let it know you are no longer needing it.

---

[67] Stalking Your Power is a class taught in Texas by Jimmie Terry

Lastly, scan your energy field. This is where crystals are great assets. Start with the chakras near the physical body and work your way through the koshers or layers all the way out to the bliss body. Ask Source to replace any areas of your energy bodies that may be irregular, void, imbalanced or depleted with pure Love, channeling it in from God.

Sit in this place of receiving for as long as you would like. Make it a regular practice of sitting in this place of deep Divine connection.

Chapter 7 Yoga 4 Love Signature Class Formats + Sequences

If you practice yoga 1 time a week you begin to change your body.
If you practice yoga 2 times a week you will begin to change your mind.
If you practice yoga 3 or more times per week you will change your life!
~Anonymous

For this part of the book, which is written like a manual, it is utilized to enhance or jump start your asana practice. You may use these sequences for your own personal mat time or for teaching others, and if you do the latter, we ask that whenever apropos please credit the source.

Some are full class sequence, some mini flows. To help you with the benefits, alignment contraindications and full photos of most of the yoga poses that we use in our classes, the asana's (pronounced 'AHhhh-sa-na', with the inflection on the first syllable, not the second, as commonly mispronounced in the west), I highly recommend downloading my companion eBook, if you have not yet, from my website, *Yoga 4 Love's Big Book of Yoga Poses, Asana 101, 201 and 301.* You can get it for free from the online store at www.yoga4love.com. It is there so you can refer to all the asanas as you go. I have removed that eBook content from this book. If you need further instruction I have many videos and audio classes for you going over this for free on my website and on my YouTube Lisa Ware Yoga 4 Love channel and on Vime @yoga4lovelisa. We also offer many live streaming classes on YouTube, plus live workshops and retreats, if you are interested.

This is a chapter on different yoga class sequences and ways you can begin to bring this practice from a mechanical alignment based 'workout' (where does my hand go, where does my foot go, oh I forgot to breathe etc.) to a place of Bhavana, the feeling, intention and higher purpose of being on your mat. But first things first! We must learn the practice! First of all, may I say, yoga is not a workout, and please try to edit your language it if you tend to call it that. Yoga is a practice. Like any practice, it takes time, intention and dedication to embody. Teaching the actual asana is really my passion. I love to see someone come from a place of not knowing yoga in their body to a place of utilizing yoga to go within, to become stronger, more confident and to express their Divine individuality, then organically sharing what they learned. This is what we call taking our yoga off the mat and into the world! Enjoy!

Basic Parts to a Hatha and Vinyasa 101 Class

Opening Salutation

Begin in a starting posture, usually seated.

Set intention with class.

Breathwork, guided Pranayama.

Warm up flow; several asanas one by one, moving with one breath per movement.

Surya Namaskar, Sun Salutation flow; move through for approximately one fifth of set class time.

Solar flow series; 3-5 breaths per standing asana, holding and flowing

Mini Vinyasa Sequence to link Solar flows together.

Solar flow series; build onto sequences starting with linking 3 to 5 poses, then adding on as you flow through each time.

Balance posture; pause your flow about half way through class, practice each side or a few times per posture.

Solar flow series bringing it down a bit.

Twist poses, may add into standing flow or twist balance postures.

Seated; bring the practice down to the Earth.

Prone; transition to the belly and do a few prone asanas.

Supine cool down; may do a slow flow or hold; cue the breath to 5-15 breaths per asana. Practice several supine poses.

Savasana; final relaxation, stay in corpse pose for at least 1/10 of class time.

Closing Salutation or a reading.

Final OM.

Basic Parts to an Intuitive Vinyasa Class

Begin the warm up flow; combining breath work, pranayama, then asana each moving with one breath per movement.

Cue for each breath, each inhale and exhale.

The second round of cueing is for proper alignment.

The third or final cue is for the feeling, or Bhavana, of the pose.

Standing Posture sequences are referred to as a 'Solar Vinyasa Flow'. This consists of about 5 to 7 asanas each linked together with breath.

Next we repeat the Solar Vinyasa Flow this time holding the poses for 3 to 5 breaths per asana. The flow continues while linking standing poses balances and twists. We may also hold postures in a hatha style or continue to move like a dance in a Mini Vinyasa Flow.

Cool down and supine flow is near the end, where we are bringing the energy down for the last quarter to 1/5 of the class. This is a great time to add in a core flow sequence.

Savasana, the best pose of all, where we use essential oils, may do a reading or play the crystal or singing bowls. This is where we use our intuition to guide what is needed for the class. During Savasana we add small simple adjustments and touch enhancements, spiritual or inspirational readings, oracle cards, angel cards and the like to enhance their experience.

The final OM concludes the practice with a closing salvation, bringing our attention back to the intention of the practice.

Intuitive Vinyasa Terms, Practice from the Heart

To clarify some of the terms used, we will begin with the Sanskrit word **Bhavana**. It is an intentional meditation technique used in yoga practice where the practitioner visualizes attaining a particular characteristic like love, compassion or peace. The practitioner can set their intention and focused energy on the Divine pure Light, Energy or Consciousness.[68]

Next, a '**Mini Vinyasa Flow**' is a sequence of asanas linked together inside an Intuitive Vinyasa class. Each of the linked asanas are poses with similar energetics and similar or complementary Vayus, or directions, of pranic energy. This Mini Flow is created organically, used and and repeated intuitively within the sequencing of the class. In many instances we can also substitute a ½ Sun Salutation, what is lazily referred to as your 'Low Flow', this is the portion of the Surya Namaskar that is not standing.

A '**Solar Vinyasa Flow**' is approximately five standing asanas connected in a flowing sequence and repeated three to five times each side.

As a general guideline to describe a class we refer to '**Yoga 101**' as a class with one to two Solar Vinyasa Flows, each with Mini Vinyasa Flows connecting them together, more designed for a simple practice and to gear for beginner yogis.

A '**Yoga 201**' consists of two to three standing Solar Vinyasa Flows with Mini Vinyasa Flows connecting in between waves. This is a class for all levels of practice. We add in some pauses for intentional breath and place in

---

[68] https://www.yogapedia.com/definition/5650/bhavana

recovery poses between the Solar Flows. For the pauses we create a space to set intention and focus in postures such as: Crocodile Pose, Cobra Wave[69], Hero's Pose, Tadasana, Downward Facing Dog, Wide Knee or Extended Child's Pose. To recover we hold for only about five to ten breaths to keep the heart rate from dropping too quickly and from newbies form getting nauseated in a heated and sweaty practice. After recovery then move back into the next Solar Vinyasa Flow, offering the class opportunities flow or stay, while listening to their body.

In an Intuitive Vinyasa Flow '**Yoga 301**' we build the class around a peak asana, like an arm balance or an inversion. We then sequence the energetics of the Mini and Solar Vinyasas intuitively or planned out to move with the direction and Vayu of the peak posture. In it we offer opportunity to move through three to four Solar Waves with two to three different Peak Asanas all in the same direction of energetic flow. You can learn more in as I discuss this sequencing and the flow of the Vayu's of energy with the different pose   in the Asana 201 chapter on the free eBook *Yoga 4 Love's Big Book of Yoga Poses, Yoga 101, 201 and 301* on our website www.yoga4love.com.

A Peak Asana or Peak Pose is the epic moment of the practice where all the other energetics build up to, and from that point the remainder of the class moves down from that place. In a Yoga 301 you may build in hills and valleys of Peak Pose energy by layering in two to three peak asanas with Mini Vinyasas or resting poses between them. This is a really fun practice and most of our Master classes and workshops are sequenced in the 301 format.

One final thought; as you develop your own adaptation of practice and style, first totally embody this practice style by hundreds of Intuitive Vinyasa hours on your own may. Then once you begin to conduct a class you have

---

[69] Adapted from the Prana Flow style by Shiva Rea

160

literally embodied your Vinyasa Flows. This is so important because you never have to stress over the planning and the timing of a class; you can build your class simply by moving intuitively with an over all intention and then watching the class. By knowing your practice by heart, with the Bhavana of the poses, and from experience of how long each Vinyasa Flow takes you to move through, you can literally place each sequence individually into your class organically and be totally present with what your class needs that day. This is the beauty of teaching from the heart of the practice. OM.

The basic yoga principles are as follows: our energy follows our thoughts and our minds. We are only as strong as our breath. All yoga posture practice, the fourth limb in the eight limbs of yoga, asana or yogasana, is built on pranayama, or breath. All yoga comes from a foundation of Hatha Yoga. Hatha has a very interesting definition: 'Ha' means sun, Surya in Sanskrit. 'Tha' means moon, or Chandra in Sanskrit; together the word. Hatha means 'forceful'. To cue for class we encourage breathing, feeling and listening to the body.

Beginner's Yoga Class Parts 1-5

The next series to explore is not in this book, but will be super helpful on your journey. It is my signature 'Beginner's Yoga Class Parts 1-5 and is free on my blog and a five classes on my YouTube channel, Lisa Ware Yoga 4 Love. It is a series of workshops with myself and my Y4L Trainee assistants giving clear instruction on video. This class features enhancements, hands-on adjustments and props. Each class we work on a set of asanas, and the handouts are on the blog on www.yoga4love.com.

This is a perfect practice to learn or deepen the knowledge and basic poses and breath for Hatha yoga. Experience the freedom in Vinyasa Flow yoga, linking movement with each inhale and exhale and your own personal energy, or prana. Learn to balance, get strong, lean and relaxed.

161

Intuitive Vinyasa Yoga 101, 201 or 301 Class Format

Warm Up Wave; intention, breathwork, Pranayama; 5 minutes

Beginning Vinyasa; each asana one breath per movement

Sun Salutations, Surya Namaskar

Core Heat Building; one asana hold and flow or Mini Vinyasa Flow with the body, 2 poses linked together with breath focused on building prana.

Solar Vinyasa Flows; One, three or five breaths per asana, adding in postures as you build.

Mini Vinyasa Flow or ½ Sun Salutation 'Low Flow'

Solar Vinyasa Flow 11 (in 201 classes)

Standing Balance, in energetic direction of the peak posture

Mini Vinyasa Flow or ½ Sun Salutation

Solar Vinyasa Flow 111 (in 201/301 Classes)

Standing Twists

Solar Vinyasa Flow 4 (in 301 and master classes)

Mini Vinyasa Flow

Cool Down Wave- 5-15 breaths per asana hold

Seated

Prone

Backbending

Twists

Inversions

Supine

Savasasana

Closing OM

Mini Vinyasa Flows, Core Heat + Prana Building Poses

Add these sequences with any Solar Vinyasa Flow as a Mini Vinyasa or to build heat and energetic direction leading up to a Peak Asana, beginning with getting the prana flowing.

Mini Vinyasa Flow, ½ Sun Salutations or Low Flow

Plank, to Chatarangua,

Upward Facing Dog landing in

Downward Facing Dog.

Option to modify this 1/2 flow by moving from Half Plank (kneeling Plank), down to the Earth like a caterpillar, chest first, then chin then belly last. Move into Cobra Wave, breathing into Cobra, head comes up last, then lowering while swaying like a snake, flowing a few times in your Cobra Wave.

Inhale into Cobra then exhale into Extended Child's pose.

Core Heat + Prana Building Flows

- Half Splits; Ardha Hanamanasana to Lunge Flow, deepening each time then holding in any stage, or Krama, of splits
- Chair: Hold in a hatha style with breath building heat
- Chair with option to flow reach and drop with breath in a flowing Body Vinyasa
- Boat to Chair Flow
- Boat Flow, Navasana with arm options, reaching behind knees, knees bent; alternating one arm one leg, or full boat
- Core Work Z Pose: start lying on your back with bent legs up, heels level with knees, knees above tail bone. Take arms behind head cupping neck, and bring elbows directly up above shoulders. Curl tailbone up and push low back into the Earth. Wrap arms into armpits. You may also balance a ball or a yoga block on shins, holding shins level with the horizon. Hold 15

breaths. Repeat at least three times, only resting head and arms between cycles[70].

- 'Happy Baby Core Pulse; start in Happy Baby, and then releases toe grip. Make Vira Mudra, index fingers pointed and fingers laced, reach up overhead and breath in. Exhale and reach hands in Vira between happy baby legs and pulse with short exhales. Repeat three cycles of ten, and do at least three cycles.

- Hollow Body, Canoe to Advanced V Ups; Begin in Boat and then lower legs and back in to a Canoe pose. Reach overhead and hold, but if low back is needing support keep hands on mat by hips. To take it up a notch come to full Canoe pose reaching and then V Up quickly on the exhales. Do as many as you can. Rest.

- Legs Up Wall with Hover; Start in Viparita Karani, Legs up the Wall. Point toes and drop legs to one side about 45 degrees from the Earth and hover. Inhale up, exhale to other side. Repeat a few times until you really feel the core engage. Make sure to move intentionally, as to engage core and protect lower back.

- Seated Spinal Twist Flow | Jathara Parivartanasana

- Vasistasana Side Plank Flow; start in all fours. Step right foot back behind left knee and left hand, placing all in a row. Pivot left toes to be at a 90 degree angle. Inhale and reach right hand to the sky. Bring more weight onto left hand and right foot making left knee loose and engaging side body into a modified Side Plank. Pull right toes toward you to bring razor edge of foot parallel with the end of your mat. Hold. Inhale, reach back up, engage Root Lock. Flow to into Gate by reaching right hand down right leg toward right foot and lifting left hand overhead like a dancer. Hold and breathe. Flow to each pose a few times then switch sides.

---

[70] Adapted from an Ana Forrest posture taught in a master class

- Dolphin Flow; Start in all fours. Bring forearms to ground and wrap middle fingers around triceps, coming almost to a Child's Pose. While grabbing opposite elbows measure where your elbows are on the mat, this is the 'I Dream if Jeannie' Pose! Then keeping elbows there, bring hands in front of you on the mat and clasp the hands around each other, not locking fingers. Tuck bottom pinkie in. Bring your toes underneath you and lift hips to Dolphin Pose. Flow lifting one leg then down with breath, lift other leg, then down with breath. Rest between flows in Child's Pose or Cat and Cow Breath in all fours.
- Down Dog to Turbo Dog; start in Extended Child's pose and measure where hands and feet are on mat with toes tucked under you and arms straight. Engage hands into Earth, Hasta Bandha. Lift hips to Downward Facing Dog without rocking forward into all fours. Use the core and keep chest pressing toward thighs, lift hips, then lower, only bending knees. Stay out of the shoulders by engaging core. Inhale, lift, exhale lower maybe just an inch or two or all the way to almost Extended Child's pose, knees hovering off mat. Rest.

Yoga 4 Love Relax + Restore Yoga 101 Format

The basic teaching of this class is that there are really no standing asanas in Yin Yoga, for the most part. If you choose to add standing poses hold and breathe and keep it light in intensity. Use the wall as your main prop! You can do a whole class on the wall. Do lots of assists and enhancements, and give and receive lots of love.

Make sure to have all props ready before class; you will need two firm folded blankets, yoga strap, two blocks and of course pure room temp water. Our intention is to turn off the muscles and get into the ligaments and deeper tissues. To do this we must be a friend to gravity and 'Fill the Space' between our body and the Earth with plenty of props so we can melt down and truly let go.

Relax + Restore Sequencing:

Set intention; Metta, cultivating Self love, Affirmation for the day

Mantra music

Pranayama; 3 part breath, Ujayii breathing

Warm up Postures

Wave 1; 3-5 poses, long holds, 5 breath min to 15+ breaths

Restorative Postures

Wave 11; 3-5 poses

Restorative Postures

Balance poses on all fours or kneeling, no standing

Twists; Seated or Supine

Pranayama | Focused poses Hero's Pose

Prone Asanas (not for Seniors or PreNatal)

Inversions (Yin- shoulderstand using wall, Legs Up Wall with strap or wall, Happy Baby)

Supine twists

Savasana with lots of love

Guided Mediation

Aromatherapy

Promotional Intro Class Sequence

Child's Pose

Knees to Chest

Supine Twist

Cat/ Cow

Spinal Balance

Lunge

Switch

Forward Fold

Monkey

Reverse Swan Dive

Mountain

Swan Dive

Forward Fold

Downward Facing Dog

Child's Pose

Down Dog

Lunge/ switch

Forward Fold

Rev. Swan

Mountain

Warrior 1

Warrior 2

Rev. Warrior

Side Angle Flow with Arms

Warrior 2

Lunge/ Switch

Downward Facing Dog

Childs Pose

Locust

Childs Pose

Roll Over/ Knees to Chest

Butterfly Supine

Legs Up Wall (strap)

Knees To Chest to Savasana

Yoga 101 Intuitive Vinyasa Basic Class Sequence

Ujayii Breathing

Alternate nostril breath

Supine spinal twist flowing one breath per movement

Core Reverse Superman Hollow Body

Forward Fold

Ragdoll

Reverse Swan Dive

Mountain

Surya Namaskar/ Sun Salutations intro and break down workshop style

Warrior 1

Warrior 2

Reverse warrior

Side Angle

Vinyasa Flow

Child's pose

All 4's

Crescent Lunge on knee, both sides with blocks

Half Splits / Ardha Hanuman

Crescent Lunge on knee to half splits flow

Mountain

Warrior 2

Triangle

Mountain

Triangle

Pyramid

Forward fold

Seated

Staff

Seated Forward fold

Bridge

Legs Up Wall

Supine Twist, both sides

Supine Butterfly

Savasana

Yoga 4 Love Lunar Slow Flow 101

Tadasana | Mountain

Samisthiti hands at heart starting posture

Swan Dive to Forward Fold; hold for a few breaths, move with intention into the flow, keeping lunar energy active. Hold three to five breaths minimum per pose.

Vinyasa Flow '½ Sun Salutation', Modified with Child's Pose

    Kneeling Plank

    Caterpillar; Chest, Chin, Belly to Earth

    Cobra Wave

    Extended Child's Pose

    Repeat a few times moving with intention to get into the flow

Downward Facing Dog

Mountain | Tadasana

Uttitha Hastasana, far reaching mountain pose

Lateral Flexion; or Kali Mudra Flow; Extend arms up, interlacing fingers, lean right, back to center, lean left flow with breath, options to take one hand down thigh or keep arms extended

Anjanyasana (Crescent Lunge) Right foot, Big step back

Crescent Lunge Twist; Extend Right hand to back of mat, open heart, option to open front hand toward top of mat arms level with horizon

Warrior 1 with Butterfly Arms

Mountain

Repeat Crescent Lunge Twist on left; Repeat flow 3 to 5 times with slow movement and breath.

Tadasana

Vinyasa Flow ½ Series

Warrior 11 Right foot back, flow with breath

Reverse Warrior to Warrior 11

Goddess Pose; High Malasana; Bring hands to heart center, bend knees over ankles

Warrior 11 turning to the back of the mat, hands at heart

Reverse Warrior bringing top hand to back of neck and reach through elbow, opening side of body to the sky. Hands to heart to Warrior 11. Repeat Goddess Pose, Warrior 11, Reverse Warrior and Warrior 11, then turn body to front of mat. Step to Warrior 1.

Mountain Pose

Vinyasa Flow ½ Series or Sun Salutation 'Low Flow' moving slow and with intention:

> Down Dog
>
> Plankasana
>
> Chatarangua
>
> Upward Facing Dog
>
> Down Dog

Forward Fold

Balance:Pose of Choice, Tree or Eagle

Malasana; Low Garland Pose

Option for Crow Bakasana prep, with breath, not building a lot of heat.

Monkey ½ Lift

Gorilla; Hand to Foot Pose; may flow Monkey to Gorilla with breath

Kneeling Plank

Caterpillar~ Lower to Ground, 'Chin chest belly'

Crocodile Pose (Rest)

Prone Pose of choice; Locust or ½ Bow then switch; or Bow with a strap.

Supine series on your own: Bridge, Supine Twist, Butterfly

Savasana; OM

Breath Cues as follows:
Inhale (in) Mountain
Exhale (ex)

Yoga 4 Love Signature Vinyasa Flow
Yoga 4 Love Signature Sun Salutation 101 Vinyasa

in Mountain

ex Swan Dive

in Half Lift

ex Forward Fold

in ½ lift (Monkey)

ex Step Right foot into lunge

in Drop knee to Earth

ex Kneeling Plank

in Kneeling Plank (opt to hold a few breaths)

ex Crocodile (chin, chest, belly)

in Cobra Wave with breath 3-5x

ex all the way back to Extended Child's pose (arms straight, elbows off ground, ball of foot tucked under body and hold)

in Down Dog

ex Forward Fold

in ½ lift Monkey Pose

ex Forward Fold

in Reverse Swan Dive

ex Mountain (opt to flow with arms)

Hold in Tadasana; Mountain

Repeat Switching Foot in Lunge

Surya Namaskar Low Flow ½ Series Modified

in Down Dog

ex Extended Child's Pose

in Kneeling Plank

ex Caterpillar (Knees Chin, Chest, Belly)

in Cobra

ex Down Dog

Repeat

Yoga 4 Love Signature Traditional Surya Namaskar 201 Vinyasa

Inhale (in) Samastithi (Starting Posture)~ Anjali Mudra, feet together, top of mat

Exhale here, finding Drishdi, eye level or higher

in Reach up Uttiha Hastasana (Far Reaching Mountain Pose, option for backbend) ex Swan Dive

in ½ lift Monkey

ex Uttanasana

in ½ lift Monkey

ex Step Right foot into lunge

in Plankasana (opt to hold a few breaths)

ex Chatarangua (watch for keeping a danda, a straight line of energy, top of head, ribs, hips, heels; keeping shoulders and elbows at 90 degree, shoulders not dropping too low)

in Urdhva Svanasana

ex Adho Svanasana

in come to tippy toes, look between thumbs

ex Jump Front Uttanasana

in ½ lift Monkey Pose

ex Forward Fold

in Reverse Swan Dive to Tadsana opt for backbend

ex Utkatasna/Chair

in Uttitha Hastasana

ex Tadasana

Repeat Switch Foot in Lunge

(Vinyasa flow for 25% of class, adding in postures to the flow)

Add in 1-2 more Standing Solar Flows, Mini Vinyasas, and Balance Posture, Peak Pose, Prone, Inversion and Supine then finish in Savasana.

Yoga 4 Love Signature Traditional Surya Namaskar 301 Vinyasa

Inhale (in) Samastithi (Starting Posture)~ Anjali Mudra, feet together, top of mat

Exhale here, finding Drishdi, eye level or higher

in Reach up Uttiha Hastasana, backbned with Vira Mudra interlocking fingers, index extended (modify hands at heart or in buttefly arms for nurturing low back)

ex Swan Dive

in ½ lift Monkey

ex Uttanasana

in ½ lift Monkey

ex Jump back Chatarangua (watch for bent elbows on jump back, danda, straight line of energy, not jumping into Plankasana for shoulder stability)

in Urdhva Svanasana

in Adho Svanasana

in come to tippy toes, look between thumbs

ex Jump Front Uttanasana

Forward Fold to ½ lift, Monkey Pose

ex Forward Fold

in Reverse Swan Dive to Far Reaching Tadsana with backbend

ex Utkatasna Chair (opt to hold and flow with arms to build prana, end on an inhale up)

ex Tadasana

Repeat 3-5x then add onto the flow

Flow with adding in additional asanas to the sequence

Begin to hold 3-5 breaths in the warrior series or added asanas after flowing

3-4 Full Solar Waves with different asanas building the energy and theme of the peak asana

Between the Solar standing series add either:

Pranam Dandasana (flat on belly from UPward Facing Dog with arms out front in Prayer, third eye onthe Earth for surrender or

Virasana for recovery and focus, if the tailbone is not on the Earth, make sure to cue sitting on 1-2 blocks or Stands on Knees as a modification

174

After a Downward Facing Dog opt to jump through into Dandasana/ Staff pose and move into a seated asana series from here

Peak Asana

Option to Flow through one or ½ of the previous built flow sequences

Peak Asana 2 (optional)

Flow

Balance Series (a more advanced balance in the same Vayu of energy that the rest of the series was built upon)

Prone Asanas

Crocodile or Pranam Dandasana

Supine Asanas

Inversion 1

Inversion 2 optional (lowering energy)

Twists

Savasana

Yoga 4 Love Signature Surya Namaskar Chi Flow Vinyasa

in Mountain

ex Warrior 1

in ex Warrior 11 Flow with body

in ex Reverse Warrior; Look up then hold in Peaceful Warrior with Drishdi at back foot

in ex Warrior 11 Flow

in ex Side Angle; Uttihta Parsvakonasana

in ex Warrior 11

Solar Flow: Repeat Warrior Flow to Side Angle on each sid. Then windmill arms down to Low Lunge, do this when energy is getting lower.

in ex Lunge

½ Sun Salutation Low Flow

in Plankasana

ex Chatarangua

in Upward Facing Dog

ex in Downward Facing Dog

ex Forward Fold

in Reverse Swan Dive

ex Chair; hold

in Mountain

Repeat Other Side

Add in 2-3 more Standing Solar Flows, Arm Balance, Mini Vinyasas, Arm Balance or Standing Balance moving into Peak Pose. Then add an option for an Inversion with all levels, karmas. Finish with Prone and Supine and a nice long, relaxing Savasana.

Yoga 4 Love Signature Warrior Heart Opening Vinyasa

in Warrior 1, butterfly arms open heart

ex Straighten Front Leg and Bring Elbows to touch, shoulder high

in Sink into Warrior 1 Reaching hands behing body and clasp hands. Inhale and exhale opening heart center.

Repeat end on an inhale

ex Warrior 11 open arms wide

in Lengthen and Reach

ex Soften and Relax turn palms up

in flow upper body forward like on a surfboard

ex flow upper body back

repeat

in Reverse Warrior place top hand behind neck and reach elbow to the sky, opening side body and armpit, finding joy!

(next time through flow add Reverse Peaceful Warrior, Turning head to look down at back foot, soften gaze and relax)

176

in using root lock lift to Warrior 11

ix settle into Virabhadrasana 11; Warrior 11 inhale here and stay

ex Windmill arms down to Lunge, turn back heel

½ Series Vinyasa:

> in Plankasana
>
> ex Chatarangua or Crocodile
>
> in Upward Dog or Cobra
>
> ex Down Dog or Childs Pose 3-5 Breaths, using 'Hahh' sigh

breathing in Down Dog)

in Down Dog

ex Forward Fold

in ½ lift

ex Forward Fold

in Reverse Swan Dive

ex Mountain Flow with Arms; repeat both sides a few times.

Yoga 4 Love Signature Warrior with Bow, Kundalini Vinyasa

in Mountain

ex Warrior 1; Virabhadrasana 1

in Arms reach forward level with the horizon, fists come together toward front of mat like holding a bow and arrow

ex Pull back bow into Warrior 11, open hips and shoulders with dynamic tension

in Face front into Warrior 1 bring Fists together

ex Pull back into Warrior 11; Virabhradrasana 11 with bow arms, squeeze shoulder blades together

in Warrior 1

ex Tadasana or Samastithi Starting Posture

repeat other side

end in Tadasana

in Warrior 1

ex Vira 11

in Reverse Warrior

ex Half Bind Bottom Arm or reach around and grab inner thigh

in Virabhradrasana 11 using Root lock

ex arms level with horizon

in reaching arm while forward pushing back hip toward bottom of mat, find furthest extension of reach

ex bottom arms reach down into Trikonasa

in reach top arm to sky in Triangle; hold 3 to 5 breaths

ex Reach up with top hand, staying in the pose, opt to use core and bring both arms into a V and hold

in Lift with top ribs using Mula Bandha

ex option to half bind or full bind in Trikonasana

in lift top arm to sky

Core up Root Lock into Warrior 11

ex Warrior 11

in Warrior 1

ex Mountain Pose

Hands to Heart Center Anjali Mudra

Step feet together into Samastithi 3-5 breaths

Repeat

Yoga 4 Love Signature Crescent Lunge Heart Opening Vinyasa

in Mountain~ Flow with arms (Lift arms out and up big inhale, exhale hands reach down by sides like making Angel Wings or moving through honey) repeat and flow 3-5 cycles of breath

in Arms Reaching Up in Mountain | Uttiha Hastasana

178

ex Step back into high crescent lunge with heel lifted off of mat, pushing off back lifted heel and energizing back knee

in lift heart bring index finger and thumb together in Jyana Mudra (making the OK sign)

ex Drop hands down by hips, sink into front thigh bringing it level with the horizon

in Lift heart look up

ex Sink into front thigh

in lift back leg straight

ex Soften into the pose

in Push off back ball of foot

ex to Mountain pose hands at heart center Anjali Mudra

in Lift arms up overhead into prayer

ex Forward Fold bringing hands through the center line of the body

in Step back into Lunge

ex Drop knee to ground and point toe into Low Lunge

in Lunge option to lift arms high

Move into lunge series or Hanumanasana flow

Half Splits to Hanumanasana Flow

ex Fold over front leg bringing it straight into Ardha Hanaman (half splits)

in bend knee Low Lunge lift arms and open heart

ex slide front heel away from back knee and surrender folding forward into Ardha Hanaman

in bend knee, lift high with arms into low lunge, Ajnasana

ex fold into Hanumanasana (cue the deepest lunge, 3/4 splits or full)

stay for a few breath cycles

Option for full Hanumanasana, (cue: lift up arms to sky with joy like the monkey God Hanuman, leaping over the ocean to serve his master for the Highest Good!)

in come out slowly to Ajnasana (low lunge on knee)

ex Kneeling Plank

(Mini flow optional)

Hero's pose Varasana Hold and rest

in all 4's Table Top

ex Lunge other side

Repeat

Lunge Flow Series in Kramas, option for Peak Asana Arm Balance

Anytime you end in a lunge you can move into the lunge options, building this into your flows one asana or two at a time

Lunge left foot back (cue for blocks)

Bring both arms to inside of front foot, right pinkie by Right big toe

Option to bring back knee down and opening Psoas (inner groin) or keep in Runner's Lunge energizing back leg

Hold here or next Krama

Bring elbows to earth

Hold here or next Krama

Bring right arm under right thigh, bend elbows into Lizard Pose

Hold her or next Krama

Running Man, cueing for Arm Balance, cue them to work on the Krama that is right for them and not look around the room. Walk around and assist.

Surya Namaskar 201 Chi Vinyasa Half Series

in Down Dog

ex in Down Dog with Pranic pulsations/ Chi Prastrations (Elements of Cat/ Cow, staying out of shoulders in pose, keeping 45 degree line of energy but flowing)

in Look between thumbs and lift tailbone to sky, bend knees deeply

ex Plankasana with Round back, look under body at naval (Nadi Drisdi), in

in Plankasana

ex Rounded Back Nadi Drishdi

repeat

in Plankasana Pull Tailbone down toward heels

ex Chatarangua, Elbows never higher than shoulders

in Urdhva Mukha Svanasan; Up Dog, open heart to the Heavens

ex with bent knees Down Dog with Chi Prastrations, like cat and cow in Down Dog

in Breathe and release, stay in down dog or move to Child's Pose or Hero's Pose

Yoga 4 Love Signature Vinyasa 201 Format

Sukasana, Simple Seated or other seated posture chosen for the class

Pranayama (3 part breath, Ujayii breathing or Alternate Nostril Breath)

Set intention (Bhavana, Connect to something greater than ourself; Affirmation/ Mantras for the day)

Vinyasa Flow (Get prana moving, one breath per movement, establishing the theme and energy direction of the class)

Surya Namaskar (Varied based on peak pose, using the Y4L different Signature Vinyasa Flows; 3-5 rounds both sides or 20-25% of the class)

Core Heat Building (Connection to Prana/Chi/Agni)

Standing Series Flow 1 (3-5 Poses each series; Warriors, Standing Asana Series etc, building on energetic Vayu of peak posture)

181

Mini Connecting Vinyasa Flow between standing series (ie: ½ flow Sun Salutation , Lateral Flexion to Forward Fold Flow, Araha Hamumanasana to Low Lunge, Cat/Cow, Staff/ Dandasana- Point and Flex ankles with Breath)

Peak Pose Krama 1 (modified stage, beginning stage arm balance or inversion prep etc.)

Standing Solar Series Flow 11 (Prana Building, Using Vayu of energy based on peak pose, 3-5 poses. ie: triangle, Half Moon, twists, etc.)

Peak Pose Krama 11 (opt to stay in Krama 1)

Standing Twists

Recovery Posture/ Drishdi Focal Point (Hero's/ Varasana, Crocodile, Child's Pose, Pranam Dandasana)

Standing Series Flow 111 (Add in if teaching a longer. Omit if a shorter class)

- For a longer class add a standing Solar Series Flow IV (Add onto the flow that you have built, only for a longer master class)

Peak Pose Krama 111 (Full Peak Pose or they can stay in Krama 1 or 2)

Mini Vinyasa Flow

Recovery Posture/ Drishdi Focus

Standing Balance Series

Mini Vinyasa Flow (if needed to transition)

Recovery Posture/ Drishdi Focus

Core Strength (Tolasana or Lolasana on blocks)

Prone Posture (3x with recovery: Pranam Dandasana or Crocodile)

Seated or Supine Twisting

Supine Poses (Ananda Balasana, Supta Padha Bandha Konasana, Supine Straddle, Supine Hand to Big Toe)

Inversions (Shoulderstand | Sarvagasana to Plow or Legs Up Wall | Viparita Karini to Happy Baby)

Heart Opening Supine Asana (Bridge, Wheel Prep or Wheel)

Fish | Matyasana (*Option to Advanced Students~ Finish with any pose Student wants to do to complete their practice 15 breaths.)

Savasana

OM

Bird of Paradise Vinyasa Flow

Mini Vinyasa Flow of choice open hips variation

Triangle

Extended Side Angle

Half Bind

Full Bind

Bird of Paradise

Step back to Lunge

Mini Vinyasa Flow of choice

Empowering Side Twist Flow

Mini Vinyasa Flow of choice closed hips variation

Begin in Mountain or Forward Fold

Chair with Hands in Anjali Mudra at heart center

Twisted Chair; lock elbow into outside of knee

Option to step back to Crescent Lunge, Twist with hands at

Lock twisted side elbow into knee and open heart to sky.

Crow Flow with Uddiyana Bandha Flow

From Side Twist to Right

Bring hands to Earth to right of the mat (may cue to center self on to mat)

Bring front left elbow onto right knee

Bring back elbow onto right hip

Come into Yogi Squat with twist (cue keeping elbows locked into the knee and hip at all times)

Inhale lift hands and rock back onto feet

Exhale rock toward right side and bring hands to Earth

Repeat Rocking with breath to bring more and more weight onto elbows

Cue exhale Uddiyana Bandha (SUPER IMPORTANT FOR FLYING, Uddiyana is the upward flying lock)

Float or fly, or continue to work on the prep.

Come out into twisted chair

Untwist and return to Tadasana or Uttanasana.

Enhancement Options during Savasana

- Guided Chakra Meditations

- Reiki Self Guided Hand Placements

- Guided Meditation; Tranquil Place: Beach, River, Mountains, Lake

- Optional Essential Oils or Aromatherapy; teachers ask students to turn right wrist up to sky if they want to receive Essential Oils.

- Hands on Loving Enhancements

- Sound Healing with recorded or live instruments

- Nature Sounds

- Head or Foot massage

- Thai Bodywork

- Play sound machine or soft music

- Awaken with sound (Bells, singing bowls etc.)

- Guided Meditation~ Tranquil Place: Beach, River, Mountains, Lake

Chapter 8 The Paths of Yoga, The Journey to Intuitive Vinyasa

Classes are ritual sadhanas, a groove to one's Self...breath inspired journeys that offer a complete spectrum (ha-tha) of rhythms from meditative and rejuvenating to the challenging and empowering. The wave of a class is created through cycles of effective and creative sequences (vinyasas) linked together through the breath-wave.

Every class is well-rounded : following the mandala of the body and asanas - to create whole body transformation of strength and fluidity, circulation and centering... Embrace the flow and allow the prana to guide you.

~Shiva Rea, founder of Prana Vinyasa

Though "Hatha" appears to be one word, it can in reality be broken down to:

- "ha" meaning effort, activity, solar side and

- "tha" meaning letting go, passivity, lunar side.

What is Hatha Yoga?

All yogas are rooted in Hatha Yoga. In Hatha yoga we attempt to balance our effort with that of release; balancing pose with repose. Going further into the depths of the word we find the "ha" as having masculine qualities while the 'tha' has feminine qualities. Not only are the qualities of active and receptive balanced but also the masculine and feminine aspects of our being are balanced, as well.

Finally, taking the process to a universal level, 'ha' becomes the sun and 'tha' the moon. The solar heat of our bodies and soul becomes balanced with that of the cool, lunar energies.

Hatha yoga cultivates a conscious awareness and sensitivity that balances out our natural tendencies for these dualistic qualities. We balance ourselves internally and calm the chaos of the conflicting impulses of the mind and thus prepare ourselves for meditation.

During a Hatha yoga practice different postures are practiced. Through these asanas, or poses, we awaken the self, the Self as the witness, watching the process as the observer and we begin to understand ourselves on a deeper level. We become the watcher watching, non-judging, observing and transcending that which we know of ourselves. At the same time we begin to awaken a deep awareness and intelligence of our bodies. We learn to watch how the skin feels when the arm moves a certain way, how the quadriceps muscles turn the bone of the femur when we engage our thighs, how the organs are cleansed, replenished with fresh blood when we twist our torso. We revive our cells and our nerves and ultimately we begin to create space in our bodies allowing for greater prana flow. This is the breath, energy or life force to moving through us. By staying connected to the breath we are invited to stay present and live in the moment.

Rituals of an Intuitive Vinyasa Class

The rituals of a our signature Intuitive Vinyasa Yoga style class are so very important. Without it we are merely teaching calisthenics. This style of teaching, from the roots of the masters, has heavily influenced my teaching journey. I have studied from the masters with private lessons. For reasons from a Higher Power I was sought out by Kumar Pallana, master yogi, actor and entertainer.[71] I built a relationship with him, he taught me the kriyas, cleansing actions, the old yogis practiced and he taught me proper form for handstand (Urshva Vrikaasana) in a very difficult and ego breaking private

---

[71] https://en.wikipedia.org/wiki/Kumar_Pallana

lesson. He came to my studio to observe me teach a class to my students and asked me many direct questions scrutinizing my teacher training and apprenticeship program (at the time it was only available in studio). He nodded his approval once he found out the depth of the studies and the length of the time my students have with me and the program. He said so many Western yoga trainings are so short, and how can you learn yoga in a few months! I am forever grateful for his lessons. Shortly thereafter he crossed over in October of 2013.

I have attended many master level classes and weekend intensives with many popular modern yogis, including Judith Lasater, Nicolai Bachman, Brian Kest, Dr. Jeff Migdow, Suzanne Sterling, Rod Stryker, Leslie Kaminoff and so many more. The majority of my deep studies theough books of ancient lineage, and my downloaded teachings from masters crossed over through Reiki, shamanic practices, drumming, chanting, meditation and many pure downloads of sequences from Spirit. I also have had the privilege of private lessons with Krishnamacharya's longest student, the one and only Srivatsa Ramaswami.

One of the most influential modern day master teachers that I have worked with is Shiva Rea. Shiva has led a path to inspire others and I have utilized these teachings as an organic guideline on a profound journey toward my style of teaching, which can be called 'Intuitive Vinyasa Flow' Yoga.

The 4 Paths of Yoga

Karma Yoga is the selfless devotion of all inner as well as the outer activities as a Sacrifice to the Lord of all works, offered to the eternal as Master of all the soul's energies and austerities.

~Bhagavad Gita

In the past two decades, yoga has moved from relative anonymity in the West to a well-recognized practice offered in thousands of studios, community centers, hospitals, gyms, and health clubs. Although yoga is commonly portrayed as a modern Western fitness trend, it's actually the core of the Vedic science that developed in the Indus Valley more than 5,000 years ago.

The word yoga derives from the Sanskrit root yuj, which means union with the source of existence or to yoke. Enlightened consciousness is also referred to as the state of enlightenment in which there is complete freedom from all conditioning and one is no longer constrained by habit, past experiences or "karma," and any forms of dogma or ideology. It is a state of spontaneous creativity, love, compassion, joy, and equanimity. These are known as qualities of the Spirit.[72] Yoga is the means of yoking our awareness to the deep rhythms that heal and integrate us in an age that challenges our inner compass to stay in the flow. [73]

Yoga has evolved and blossomed over thousands of years, and numerous forms, styles and schools of yoga have developed. Traditionally there are four types of yoga:

- Jyana or Gyan Yoga - The yoga of the intellect, science, and knowledge

- Bhakti Yoga - The yoga of love and devotion

- Karma Yoga - The yoga of service and action

------

[72] Excerpts from The Essence of Yoga by Deepak Chopra, M.D.

[73] Quote from Shiva Rea Prana Flow Yoga

- Raja Yoga - The yoga of meditation, physical poses, and breathing practices

Raja yoga is most commonly referred to as the 'royal path of yoga'. It focuses on practices that take our awareness inward and promote the integration of the mind, body, and spirit. The classic text on raja yoga is the Yoga Sutras, attributed to the legendary sage Patanjali. While the exact dates of Patanjali's life and writings remain fuzzy, scholars estimate that the Yoga Sutras were written at least 1,700 years ago.

The four main paths of Yoga: Karma Yoga, Bhakti Yoga, Raja Yoga and Jnana Yoga are each suited to a different temperament or approach to life. All the paths lead ultimately to the same destination. They all are paths to union with Spirit, Source, Brahman, God. The lessons of each of them need to be integrated if true wisdom is to be attained.

Swami Sivananda recognised that every Yogi, or human being for that matter, possesses and identifies with each of these elements: Intellect, heart, body and mind. He therefore advocated everyone to practice certain techniques from each path. This came to be known as the Yoga of Synthesis. He also taught that in accordance with individual temperament and taste one can emphasize the practice of certain Yogas over others.[74]

Principles of Alignment, Ritual and the True Feeling of Yoga

Inhale, and God approaches you.
Hold the inhalation, and God remains with you.
Exhale, and you approach God.
Hold the exhalation, and surrender to God.
~Krishnamacharya

---

[74] http://www.sivananda.org/teachings/fourpaths.html#karma

In Hatha Yoga postures are expressed using alignment and anatomy. The challenge is how to learn and teach these principles. The goal of an alignment based practice is to help create the optimal position for the body during movement, as well modifications and enhancements to utilize while holding poses. A system developed by Beth Shaw, Founder of YogaFit is called the 'Seven Principles of Alignment' or SPA. The idea is to increase safety while simultaneously providing functional mechanical principles that participants can use in their daily life.

The true feeling of yoga is called Bhava. This is a deep yogic concept that extends to all of life that forms internal foundation from which all yoga experience arises and flourishes. Bhava is a whole mind, body experience that people experience, sometimes called being in the Flow or in a Zen state. It happens with athletes, dancers, artists, musicians, yogis and really anyone who is bringing the power of inner awareness to the state they are experiencing. To practice pure technique without bhava is like food without taste, it is dry and unappealing. It becomes a rote practice. The pleasure and joy comes from the inner state of awareness. It is this deep connection that brings transformation and satisfaction to the flow of yoga.

Through true Vinyasa the karmas, the stages of development, are introduced and nurtured. These stages move us through beginner foundational alignment, toward the doorways of growth, into to a place of pure Pranic alignment and true bliss. Intuitive Vinyasa classes are sequenced around the theme and direction of the vayu, utilizing lines of energy of the asana to enhance and awaken the individual.

We add in peak poses, challenging asanas, in a way that allows every student to find their personal beauty in that moment without any need to compare or judge where we are or where we were last week, month or year. We also focus on letting go of the outcome or the final pose and truly enjoy the present moment. We utilize many tools such as chanting, visualization, chakras, reiki and focus on the breath, pranayama.

The emphasis is on on the fluidity, breath and the inner state of focused moving meditation within the flow. A true Vinyasa class has those dimensions that create the state of flow: We connect fully to our experience through our breath, our thoughts, our emotions, our dynamic movement and the group collective energy of the class. We are open to the power of the community while attending to our own flow. Move together.

Conscious music is used as a tool to keep the rhythm, flow and focus of the class. Yoga is literally a moving meditation.

Hatha yoga uses the body to access the mind. Our body is our map of our self. It tells our stories. It is practical, tangible. Here and now. When our body aches or hurts, our entire well being is affected. Likewise, when our body feels good, when everything inside us is functioning and performing as it should be, our energy reflects that good feeling.

During a Hatha or Vinyasa yoga practice many various postures are practiced. These postures allow us to use the body as a vehicle for inner exploration. In this way the practice of asana is really more like praying with the body in order to reach the Divine within. One's practice can be an offering, a complete surrender; a moving meditation. By constantly moving in to the observer seat, one becomes the watcher, watching the process without judgment. The body is active. The brain is passive. The body does. The mind is.

Hatha yoga is the process of penetrating from the outermost sheath of the body, the skin and the physical body, deep down into the innermost core of the body, the bliss body, the divine body. Then we can pass through the porthole created in our practice, travel along this clear path and move into and out of this space at will.

The literal translation of Hatha is 'forceful'. But this force is not a physical force disrespecting the body, but rather an internal force involving an intensity, a burning desire to connect to something greater and beyond.

Hatha Yoga Symbolism, Tapas, the Sun and Moon

Asana must have the dual qualities of alertness and relaxation.
~ Yoga Sutra of Pantanjali 2.46

This force in Hatha yoga is called Tapas, the sense of true passion, determination and discipline, Ha and Tha together take on the meaning 'Forceful'.

It is an inner yearning, an inexplicable burning desire. Tapas helps us to free oneself from suffering and to reach a state of Samadhi, or blissful Oneness with the Universe coming to a place of Self-realization. This is the ultimate achievement of our yoga practice, that place of spiritual bliss. As we delve down into the innermost core of the Self we then emerge, purified with the fire of Tapas, allowing us to shine this Divine Light into the world.

The principle followed in the study of Hatha Yoga is that of balancing the two complementary energies that affect all life on earth. Optimal health is seen as a result of this perfect and intricate balance. A similar principle is seen to be contained in the Chinese symbolism of Yang /Yin by which the harmony of natural forces in the universe is maintained.

Regarding the philosophy behind Hatha Yoga, it is understood that ideally, in perfect health, a male predominantly expresses the qualities attributed to the Sun and a female predominantly expresses the qualities of the Moon. The masculine energy develops the body for outward expression through strength and power. The feminine qualities emphasize flexibility, beauty and grace in her natural physical expression.

192

In reference to these physical characteristics are the qualities and personality traits associated with them, therefore man in his self culture patterns himself to have the desired attributes of strength of mind, will, and leadership; a woman predominantly seeks to express beauty, nurturing and kindness.

If each individual lives in accordance with this basic principle ordained by Nature, then it is likely that health will be assured because of the appropriate polarity of energies that are generated and conducted through the glandular system of the body and the nervous system. There is little argument against the male/female division of the sexes being representative of the electro/magnetic energies which can be closely seen to relate to the positive and negative currents in electricity.

From a spiritual point of view as the soul is neither male nor female, these are only human qualities. Therefore, both the ideal male and ideal female must in time be embodied if we are to evolve and raise the frequency of this planet.

Solar and Lunar Qualities, Hatha Yoga Philosophy

Your body exists in the past and your mind exists in the future. In yoga, they come together in the present. ~B.K.S. Iyengar

HA: Solar, the sun

Gold is the metal of the Sun

Energies are positive and electric:

A constant radiance of energy

Actively shines by day

Creative power

Masculinity

Consciousness

193

Heat

Represents fire

Strength

Symbolizes the spirit

Practicality

Represents reason

The Sun commands

Rules the visible world

The Sun represents universality

THA: Lunar, the moon

Silver is the metal of the Moon

Energies are receptive and magnetic:

A cyclic radiance waxing and waning

Actively shines by night

Femininity

Sub-conscious or unconscious

Cool

Represents water

Gentleness, subtlety

Represents the soul

Idealistic

Intuitive

Encouraging

The Moon rules the invisible worlds

The Moon represents the particular

Both Sun and Moon energies are powerful are required for the growth of all living things. Warmth and moisture are needed for all progress and growth on all planes of being. This is ideally demonstrated in the germination of seeds where water is needed to swell the seed and warmth to motivate growth.

There is much importance of both the solar and lunar energies in regard to our existence on this planet. The sun properties are more obvious as we rely on the power of the sun to sustain our life on Earth. However, without the moon we would have no tides or movement of the waters, we would have no growth of plants and other living things as we know them, we would have no procreation of species of humans or animals and without rain and moisture, the sun would become the cause of our destruction.[75]

The Sun represents the Father

He is paternal, commanding, directing the energies of man. He motivates the individual towards the asserting of his better and nobler self.

Regarding life on our Earth, the Sun represents the Creator or Supreme Intelligence beyond which, as we understand through astronomy, exist other and superior suns in a continuance without end.

Our Moon is our Mother

She confines our energies to our earthly home, gently encouraging us to reflect and to learn to manifest our full potential.

We name many of our yoga flows after the sun and the moon. Surya Namaskar is the salute to the Sun. This is the primary foundational practice of Vinyasa. We practice for the full and new moons. The cycles of the moon

---

[75] http://essence-of-yoga.net/sun-moon-hatha-yoga-symbolism

and sun are rhythms that keep us in alignment with our intrinsic Cosmic nature.

In addition, the breath is consistently observed in our practice, and so is the mind and its thoughts. Through observation and perhaps a change in thought, or a letting go of a certain thought pattern, the experience of the pose, and ultimately the self, may transform. Each time we get on the mat we discover how different poses alter our experience of life and give us a greater understanding of ourselves off the mat..[76]

Regardless of which asana we are practicing, it always has two qualities, solar and lunar, Ha and Tha. This is reflected as alertness without tension, and relaxation without heaviness or dullness. Every pose feels strong, steady, grounded and joyful, light and playful.

Yoga is for anyone and every Body. On the physical and psychological level the body gains tremendous benefits. Yoga can help to cure ailments, prevent dis-ease, strengthen, purify and balance the endocrine, nervous and circulatory systems. With regular Ha-tha yoga practice we gain greater endurance, flexibility, and improve our posture. The body's natural weight is maintained and the organs are detoxified. Attention to the breath becomes second nature and breathing becomes easier. Energy is renewed, while blood pressure returns to normal and stress becomes easier to cope with. Thoughts become more pleasant and negative emotions diminish. In essence overall with a healthy and regular yoga practice we gain vibrant physical and emotional health and we feel calmed, peaceful and connected.

---

[76] http://iyengaryogaaspen.com/hathayoga.html

Chapter 9 Clean Eating, Healthy Living, and Ayurveda 101

Light is the manifestation of the Tejas Tattva (the luminiferous ether) within the atmosphere, that is, matter is brought into the correct visual vibration for us to perceive it. ~ Rama Prasad

The Tattvas, the 5 Elements, an Introduction and Brief History

In yoga this is called the Tattvas, which is Sanskrit. Tattvas are a way of directly experiencing the five elements. The student is now taught a method of directly learning the "theoretical" structure of the elemental worlds.

The word Tattva is comprised of two words, Tat, meaning that, and Tvam, meaning thou.. Tattva basically means 'thatness'; or the real being of anything. It is generally translated as meaning quality.

Tat represents the Godhead and Tvam the individual, giving a meaning of That, which is the Universe, art thou. This is similar to the Shamanic Native declaration of 'As above, so below, Aho!'. It is directly related to the concepts of the Macrocosm, Tat or Godhead, and Microcosm, Tvam, or individual.

The Hatha Yoga School of Tattvic Philosophy links the energy found in breathing (Prana) with the cycle of the five Tattvas. It is written within this work that "The Universe came out of the Tattvas".

The Tattvas are the five modifications of the Great Breath, Prana, which is described as the life principle of the Universe, or macrocosm and man the microcosm. Prana consists of an ocean of the five Tattvas.

The seven energy centers in the body are called chakras, and are in direct connection with the five Tattvas or the elements. The chakra system is part of the five-fold division of esoteric symbolism for categorizing the Universe.[77]

The Tattvic Philosophy in Western Tradition

The Tattvas are the astral form of the Elements, upon which the physical elements are based. The process of how the Tattvic elements become manifest is a complex process.

1. From the Sun, a 'solar wind' constantly streams forth.
2. It is a partially electromagnetic nitrous gas, which is very subtle and non-physical in nature.
3. This is the Prana (Life Matter) of the Eastern Mysteries.
4. The Earth's magnetic field captures this incorporeal nitre as the wind streams past our planet.
5. This unmanifest substance circulates around the planet in a series of fivefold waves, each of which comprises five sub-waves.
6. These waves are constantly rising and falling. It becomes more and more physical as it passes through our atmosphere.
7. A salt is formed as this nitre passes through water vapor.
8. This is "a most subtle virgin earth," the Prima Materia of the alchemists.

The Science of the Rhythm of Energy Flow on Mother Earth

The rhythm starts at sunrise and flow from Spirit, to Air, to Fire, to Water, to Earth. Each sub-Tattva takes four minutes and 48 seconds to transit a given spot. It takes a total of 24 minutes for each main Tattva. It takes a

---

[77] John Cross https://magicalpath.net/an-introduction-to-tattvas

total of two hours for a primary flow of all five Tattvas to transit. The Earth's electromagnetic field and ley lines are vitalized by these currents.

All five Tattvas are considered to be 'ethers.' The atoms of the ether bring the atoms of the atmosphere into the necessary state of vibration for us to perceive it. Each of the Tattvic ethers is related to one of the five senses.

The 5 Tattvas

- **Akasha~** is associated with the Spirit of Western Tradition
    - It is the "soniferous" ether (sound).
- **Vayu~** is the "tangiferous" ether (touch).
    - It is associated with the element of Air in Western Tradition.
- **Tejas~** is the "luminiferous" ether (sight/light/colour).
    - It is associated with the element of Fire in Western Tradition.
    - The Fire of Tejas is considered to be Agni, which is the Vedic sacrificial fire and the interior fire of Kundalini Yoga.
- **Apas~** is the "gustiferous" ether (taste).
    - It is associated with the element of Water in Western Tradition.
- **Prithivi~** is the "odoriferous" ether (smell).
    - It is associated with the element of Earth in Western Tradition.

Ayurveda 101

We are all made up of these 5 elements. We are all stars!!! Everything in our bodies and being is a balance or an imbalance of these elements. I highly encourage you to take a deeper study into Ayurveda!

In Ayurveda we study the elements to create the perfect balanced state of mind, body and Spirit. This balanced state is Sattva. We are always striving for the Sattvic balance, with our actions, our choices and most importantly the foods we put into our bodies.

The basic constitutions of the bodies are made up into three categories. We all consist of each of these three in various, changing proportions. They are know as Vata, Pitta and Kapha.

The Three Constitutons

These three constitutions represent the elements in the body.

Vata:

Air and Ether

Pitta

Fire and Water

Kapha:

Earth and Water

Substances that are predominantly composed of Ether and Air have very dynamic properties and effects and these are called 'vata substances.' Substances perform digesting, metabolizing, and transforming functions and are called 'pitta substances.' Kapha substances are made of water and earth elements and have the functions to support, lubricate and secrete.

When you are aware of what elements a substance is made of you begin to understand the kinds of effects it produces. These effects may be described in terms of the attributes.

You may be interested in taking an online quiz or two to determine your constitutions. Learning the elements and their attributes can help you to understand why a certain effect is produced in your own body. You can use this same logic to counterbalance an effect using oils, foods, herbs or activities that contain its opposite attributes, which brings complete sattvic balance, optimal health and lack of dis-ease.

There are many benefits to learning and using the elements and their attributes in this way. Through Ayurveda, which has been studied as a science for thousands of years, we now have clearer understanding of the realm of cause and effect, anatomy and physiology, structure and function.[78]

Whole Food Eating and Shopping Guide

Next we are taking a look at clean and whole food eating. This is really several parts: Lifestyle, Education, Whole Food Eating, Nutrition + Cleansing the body. For conciseness we will focus on what we put into our bodies. Let's start with what to look for at the grocery store. For a full detailed program please go to my website and download the free eBook the 21 Days to Feeling Fit Guide Book. This is intended to help you on your journey toward aclean eating and healthy living lifestyle with accountability.

Whole Food Shopping Overview

The number one things to remember when shopping for your program is do not get overwhelmed. We all start somewhere! Most supermarkets and grocery stores now have healthier food choices, organic brands and a designated aisle just for health food. Do not feel like you need a Health Food Store to find the food or the ingredients you need to start your program. However, if you do have a local health food store such as Whole Foods Market.

If you are going to a health food store to shop for the first time, make sure you have time to look around and plan on asking for help. Everyone that works in these stores is ready to help and is very knowledgeable.

---

[78] Ayurveda.com

When you make your shopping list for the first week, start with the foods you already love. Ease into the program on food you are familiar with and enjoy eating. You will eventually want to switch to cage free eggs, free range poultry, grass fed beef. Look for organic high fiber carbohydrates, fruits and vegetables whenever possible. This way we are not ingesting toxins with the foods we eat.

To begin simply follow the meal plan provided when making your list: this makes it easier when going to the store the first time. A list keeps you on track, helps you remember everything you need and keeps you from feeling lost.

Find a Coach! Find Your Tribe!

A good coach may be just what you need to help you transition. Depending on where you are and where you want to be, this leap may seem too much to do on your own. It is always a great idea to hire a professional nutritionist, life or health coach! At Yoga 4 Love we offer free mini coaching consultations, you may book your own convenient time on our website lifecoaching page!

An accountability group is a great asset. A good group will consist of like minded people, a strong and supportive leader, and a plan that not only makes sense to you, but is safe and scientifically researched. There are many out there that may be a good fit for you.

Begin or Find a Program!

Looking into all the different programs online and through books can be time consuming, expensive, tricky and confusing. If you are looking for a place to plug into with like minded people please contact us at Yoga 4 Love! We have a page on our website at www.yoga4love.com for the Healthy Living Tribe and we offer webinars, online groups, resources for clean eating, detox and cleansing, monthly challenges, as well as a maintenance and lifestyle group.

Eat Tons of High Quality, Clean, Whole Foods!

We all know we need to do this. But with so many packaged and processed foods we are a country of high caloric malnourished people. No wonder there is so much 'dis-ease' prevalent in our society.

Did you know that the recommended daily serving amount for a normal person is 9-13 servings of fruits and veggies? For athletes it is 13-18! A serving is the size of your fist. How many days last week did you get 9-13 fruits and veggies in? Last month? Last year? You get my point. It is really hard.

I recommend utilizing Juice Plus. What is Juice Plus? Juice Plus+ products are made from the juice powder concentrates and oils from 48 different fruits, vegetables and grains. While Juice Plus+ isn't a substitute for eating fruits and vegetables, their whole food-based products support a healthy diet by offering a much wider variety of naturally occurring vitamins, along with antioxidants and phytonutrients found in fruits and vegetables. Every Juice Plus+ product is made from quality ingredients grown farm fresh, providing the natural nutrients your body needs. As of the publication of this book, there are over 38 published medical studies on Juice Plus in more than 20 prestigious medical and scientific journals.[79]

Clean Eating Shopping Tips

BUY ORGANIC

Fresh, frozen or if needed, buy canned. There is usually an organic alternative to everything, just do your homework. If you want, you can shop

---

[79] https://www.juiceplus.com/us/en/clinical-research/

online first so you know what is available before you ever step foot inside the store.

Do not stick to just one supermarket. Explore your options. Note the differences in price lists from store to store and keep a look out for the sales. Sign up for any mailing lists that will keep you informed of price cuts and special offers.

What to Look For at the Grocery Store

DRY GOODS

These are a healthy alternative and can be prepared easily without additives.

LEAN PROTEINS

Organic cage-free, hormone-free and free-range meats are found in meat markets, health food stores, Costco, Whole Foods, Ann's Health Food, Cox Farms, farmers markets, co-ops. Only buy organic grass-fed beef and organic chicken. As for fish, purchase wild (never farmed) fresh or canned (in water or olive oil), Cage free organic eggs.

HEALTHY FATS

Use Extra Virgin Olive Oil (EVOO) in salad dressings and for low heat sautéing. Use Coconut Oil or grapeseed for high heat cooking high heat sautéing. Olive oil turns rancid (becomes toxic) under medium high heat, whereas grapeseed oil or Coconut Oil maintains its integrity when heated. Coconut oil is solid at room temperature. It is most often sold in jars alongside all the standard bottled oils. Avoid high-oleic safflower, corn, and canola oils as they are highly processed and most often contain GMO's. Enjoy small servings of avocado, coconut milk, olives, raw nuts and seeds (often sold at a lower price in the bulk foods section or at Costco).

HIGH FIBER CARBOHYDRATES

FRESH! Look for beautiful squishy nutrient rich veggies like squash, artichokes, leeks, okra, pumpkin or sweet potato. Enjoy experimenting with new grains, legumes and vegetables. When shopping always look for the freshest, least processed foods.

BULK

This is a great way to shop for nuts, legumes (lentils and beans), brown rice. spices, quinoa and other grains. Buying bulk is a great way to eat on a budget and also decrease waste, especially if using our own jars or other reusable containers.

DRY PACKAGED

Legumes and grains such as brown rice are often packaged and sold in ethnic or health food sections of grocery stores. Whole Foods even has vacuum sealed packaged cooked brown rice; add diced veggies and Extra Virgin Olive Oil (EVOO) for a delicious grain salad.

FROZEN

Look for cooked squash, artichoke hearts, lima beans and other veggies.

CANNED

Watch out for high sodium. Read the labels and compare, beans, artichoke hearts in water, organic soups and organic broths.

REFRIGERATED

Look for Hummus, salsa, rice tortillas, cooked lentils, grain salads and pesto.

LOW GLYCEMIC INDEX FRUITS + NON-STARCHY VEGETABLES

Look for the freshest most beautiful produce you can find. Choose a variety of colors, textures and tastes. Add healthy servings of greens (spinach, kale, Swiss chard, arugula, etc)to every meal! Explore fresh herbs like basil, cilantro, rosemary, lavender and sage Find the joy in eating low on the food chain directly from the Earth.

Most stores have an organic produce section but for a wider variety of organic fruits and vegetables, visit your local Farmers Market for farm fresh veggies (many are not organic, though) or Healthy Food Stores. Frozen organic fruits and vegetables are a great alternative when fresh is not available.

Optimal Food Choices List

LEAN PROTEIN

Juice Plus+ Complete Whole Food as a drink, shake or smoothie

Organic chicken and turkey

Wild caught cold water fish: Wild Salmon, Halibut, Cod, Mackerel, etc. NO Shellfish, Catfish or Bottom Feeders

Grass Fed Lean Red Meats, (1 x per week),

Wild Game

Cage Free and Organic Eggs

Vegan choices

HEALTHY FATS

Raw nuts and seeds (no peanuts), macadamia nuts, freshly ground flaxseed, olive oil, olives, flaxseed oil, cod liver oil, avocado, coconut milk, almond milk and almond butter, grapeseed oil

HIGH FIBER CARBS

Squash (acorn, butternut, winter), artichokes, leeks, lima beans, okra, pumpkin, sweet potato or yam and turnips

Legumes: black lentils, adzuki beans, cow peas, chick peas, French beans, kidney beans, lentils, mung beans, navy beans, pinto beans, split peas, white beans, yellow beans, brown rice, quinoa, hummus and millet

FRUIT GLYCEMIC INDEX

Low: Gl-Blackberries, blueberries, boysenberries, elderberries, raspberries, strawberries, green apples.

Moderate: Gl-Cherries, pears, apricots, melons, oranges, peaches, plums, grapefruit, pitted prunes, red apples, avocados, kiwi, lemons, limes, nectarines, tangerines, passion fruit,, persimmons and pomegranates.

High Gl-(avoid during the Detox phase) Bananas, pineapples, grapes, watermelon, mango and papaya. *Only after yoga/workout are these acceptable during your detox phase. Blend into a smoothie with Juice Plus Complete Powder for more whole foods, 13 grams of plant protein and 8 grams of fiber.

NON STARCHY VEGETABLES

*RULE: Eat no white bread/potatoes etc.

DO Eat:

Arugula, asparagus, bamboo shoots, bean sprouts, beet greens, bell peppers, broad beans, broccoli, Brussel sprouts, cabbage, cassava, carrots, cauliflower, celery, chayote fruit, chicory,chives, collard greens, cucumber, jicama (raw), jalapeno peppers, kale, kohlrabi, lettuce, mushrooms, mustard greens, onions, parsley, radishes, eggplant, endive, fennel, garlic, ginger root, green beans, hearts of palm, radicchio, snap beans, snow peas, shallots, spinach, spaghetti squash, summer squash, Swiss chard, tomatoes, turnip greens and watercress.

Whole Food Mean Breakdown

Main Dishes: Lean proteins, high fiber carbohydrates and non-starchy vegetables

Side Dishes: Low glycemic index fruits and healthy fats

WHEN EATING

Think lean protein and greens, big leafy salad, steamed veggies and your choice of Quinoa or an organic meat, wild salmon or wild caught cold water fish, grass fed beef, chicken, eggs, turkey, legumes with brown rice, quinoa or amaranth.

Serving Size: 3 ounces for women and 4 ounces for men

A Commonly Missed Topic, Our Skin!

This is our largest organ! Be observant of what we put into it!

SKIN AND BODY CARE

Remove all products that have chemical ingredients. This is a big clearing process and can be done gradually. We could really spend hours on this subject alone. Obviously, the faster that you remove the use or chemicals on your skin, the faster you will begin to detox. The skin is the largest organ and we constantly bombard it with artificial fragrances, colors, lotions with petro-chemicals (aka 'Mineral oil' and many other names, and pretty much every product from a Bath and Body Works).

Avoid aluminum found in deodorants which is a known link to breast cancer, parabens and sulfates in shampoos and conditioners and much more that we put on our body. Look for products that have ingredients that you can pronounce. Most likely you will begin to shop for beauty products at the local health food store instead of at the naturalist's worse enemy, Wal-Mart.

Watch where you spend your money and you will support the process of creating a cleaner body and a cleaner planet! We can do this one purchase at a time!

Remember, the toxic lifestyle is very much overlooked and taken for granted in the Western culture. You may feel like you are swimming upstream, but slowly and surely you will see the huge positive impact on your own body's health and energy levels, then the health of your family. The ripple will begin to widen! Your mentor Is always just a text, call or phone or email away!

Whole Food Pantry Makeover

WHAT TO BUY

Bob's Red Mill Brown Rice Flour

Flax Seeds

Chia Seeds

Bob's Reds Mill Gluten Free Oatmeal Grape Seed Oil

Bulk Foods: Dry Beans, Grains, Nuts, Seeds

Herb's & Spices

Braggs Liquid Amino (for flavoring stir frys and salads)

Organic Tamari (wheat Free, Gluten Free)

Edward & Sons Brown Rice Crackers

"Food should Taste Good" Products

Sweet Potatoes

Chips & Flaxseed Chips

Bulk Pecans and walnuts, pine nuts, cashews, almonds

Bulk Dried Beans and Lentils

Healthy Gluten Free Flours

Zucchini

Ginger

Steamed Beets

Cooked Lentils

Roasted Flaxseeds

Cauliflower

Olive Oil

Green Beans, Parsley, Dill, Chives

Veggie Chop (veggies chopped up to add to salads or quinoa

Rice Cheese

Meat alternative Products; low processed

Organic Quinoa

Quinoa GF Pasta

Organic Chicken Broth (8 pack)

Almond Butter

Organic Eggs

Sliced Mushrooms

Organic Spinach

Healthy Gluten Free Crackers (Mary's Gone Crackers)

Carrots

Organic Salsa (made without vinegar)

Celery (Great with Almond Butter)

Organic Hummus

Organic Frozen Strawberries

Nori Seaweed Sheets in the snack area (to make sushi or burritos)

Organic Frozen Berry Mix

Tasty Bite Instant Meals Ready to Eat - Punjab Eggplant, Chickpeas, Lentils

Tasty Bite - Bombay Potatoes

Raw Nuts (in the snack area)

Huge Jar of Organic EV Coconut Oil

Organic Chicken Breasts

Organic Sugar (after the 90 Days)

Green Apples

Frozen Wild Salmon

Frozen Orange Roughy Fillets

Brown Rice Pasta

Sea Salt~ Himalayan Pink in a Grinder

Ms. Mary's Cashew Crunch

Extra Virgin Olive Oil "EVOO" - cold pressed

Canned organic no sugar Tomatoes

UNREFRIGERATED PRODUCE, FROZEN SECTION, DAIRY ALTERNATIVE SECTION

Cherry Tomatoes

Frozen Organic Berries for smoothies

Unsweetened Almond Milk

Green Apples

Frozen Organic Veggies Coconut Milk

Organic Lemons

Avocados in a bag

Frozen Wild Salmon, Ahi Tuna, Halibut, Tilapia, etc

Frozen Wild Salmon Burgers

REFRIGERATED PRODUCE, CANNED GOODS, DRY GOODS

Garlic ~ Minced in bulk

Bagged Lettuce

Sliced Mushrooms

Broccoli Slaw

Shredded Cabbage

Sugar Snap Peas

Butternut Squash

Frozen Buffalo Burgers

Frozen Brown Rice

Frozen Chili Lime Chicken

Coconut Milk

Sardines

Wild Salmon

Oysters

Olives & Capers

Pumpkin

Sweet Potatoes

Squash Puree

Quinoa

Brown Rice

Brown Rice Pasta

Organic no sugar Tomatoes

Stevia in a huge box

Herbs and Spices

Almond Butter

Frozen Sweet Potato Spears (great as fries with olive oil & sea salt)

CEREAL AISLE, REFRIGERATED MEATS

Roasted Flax Seeds

Free Range Whole Chicken

Ground Flax Meal

Free Range Ground Turkey

Sprouted Brown Rice Smoked Salmon

Seaweed & sesame seed

Brown Rice

Lastly, it is great to own a small personal blender for shakes at work or travel. A Vitamix or Blentec blender is a real essential for the kitchen. It is a bit of an investment but you can use it for making soups, smoothies, sauces and so much more!

ENJOY RESEARCHING!

Chapter 10 Eight Limbs, The Yamas and Niyamas, History of Yoga

Yoga does not just change the way we see things, it transforms the person

who sees.

~ B. K. S. Iyengar

What are the Eight Limbs of Yoga?

According to the Yoga Sutras of Patanjali, one of the ancient texts that is often cited as a source for the philosophy behind yoga, there are eight limbs or branches; Ashtanga in Sanskrit: 'Ashta' is eight, 'angha' is arm or limb. Each limb relates to an aspect of achieving a healthy and fulfilling life, and each builds upon the one before it. You may be surprised to hear that only one of the limbs involves the yoga postures or asanas. [80]

The Eight Limbs begin with the Yamas and Niyamas, which are the first two limbs. They are like a map written to guide us upon our jouney through life. They are as follows:

1. The Yamas:

These are the five ethical guidelines regarding moral behavior towards others:

- Ahimsa: non-violence to all sentient and non sentient beings
- Satya: truthfulness
- Asteya: non-stealing
- Brahmacharya: non-excessiveness (often interpreted as celibacy)

---

[80] Light on Life, B.K.S. Iyengar, 2005; Yoga: The Iyengar Way, Mira Silva and Shyam Mehta, 1990

- Aparigraha: non-possessiveness, non-greed.

2. The Niyamas:

These are the five ethical guidelines regarding moral behavior towards oneself:
- Saucha: purity
- Santosha: contentment
- Tapas: self-discipline, training your senses
- Svadhyaya: self-study, inner exploration
- Ishvara Pranidhana: surrender (to God)[81]

3. Asana:

This is the practice of yoga postures. It should be noted that in the time of Patanjali the word asana meant seat. The advent of modern yoga postures happened much later.

4. Pranayama:

This is the practice of yogic breath or breathing exercises.

5. Pratyahara:

This is the withdrawal of the senses. In mastery of Pratyahara the exterior world is not a distraction from the interior world within oneself.

6. Dharana:

---

[81] https://kripalu.org/resources/yoga-s-ethical-guide-living-yamas-and-niyamas

This is deep focus or concentration; the ability to focus on something, uninterrupted by either external or internal distractions.

7. Dhyana:

This is complete meditation and builds upon Dharana, the concentration is no longer focused on a single point but is now all encompassing.

8. Samadhi:

This is total Divine Bliss. Samadhi builds upon all the other limbs and the mastery of Dhyana. Samadhi is the transcendence of the self through meditation. This is the merging of the Highest Self with the Universe, sometimes translated as enlightenment. [82]

A Complete Overview of Yoga History

We might already have an idea of what yoga is but to understand it better, we have to know what it has become in modern times, as well have knowledge in its roots and beginnings. A quick look at the history of Yoga will help us appreciate its rich tradition and who knows, it might help us incorporate yoga into our lives.

Although yoga is said to be as old as human civilization, there is no physical evidence to support this claim. Early archaeological evidence of yoga's existence could be found in stone seals which depict figures of yoga asana. This first real evidence place yoga's existence around 3000 B.C.

Scholars, however, have a reason to believe that yoga existed long before that and have traced its beginnings in actual Stone Age Shamanism. Both Shamanism and yoga have similar characteristics, particularly in the

---

[82] http://yoga.about.com/od/theyogasutras/p/eightlimbs.htm,Yoga Journal

efforts to improve the human condition. Also, both ancient practices aimed to heal the community and tribe members. Another similarity is that practitioners of both yoga and Shamanism acted as religious mediators. Although we currently now know yoga as focusing more on the journey of self, it started out as community-oriented practice before it turned inward.

Therefore, as a more accurate discussion of the history of yoga, let's divide it into four periods:

1. Vedic Period

2. Pre-Classical Period

3. Classical Period

4. Post-Classical Period.

Vedic Period

The existence of the Vedas marks this period. The Vedas is the sacred scripture of Brahmanism that is the basis of modern-day Hinduism. It is a collection of hymns which praise a Divine power. The Vedas contains the oldest known yogic teachings. The teachings found in the Vedas are characterized by rituals and ceremonies that strive to surpass the limitations of the mind and referred to as Vedic Yoga.

During this time, the Vedic people relied on Rishis, dedicated Vedic Yogis, to teach them how to live in divine harmony. Rishis were also gifted with the ability to see the ultimate reality through their intensive spiritual practice.[83] It was also during this time that Yogis living in seclusion (in forests) were recorded.

Pre Classical Period

---

[83] www.abc-of-yoga.com

The creation of the Upanishads begins the Pre-Classical Yoga. The 200 scriptures of the Upanishads describe the inner vision of reality resulting from devotion to Brahman, or Divine Bliss. These explain three subjects: the ultimate reality (Brahman), the transcendental self (atman), and the relationship between the two. The Upanishads further explain the teachings of the Vedas.

Pre Classical Yoga shares some historically traceable characteristics with both Hinduism and Buddhism. During the sixth century B.C., Buddha started teaching Buddhism, which stresses the importance of meditation and the practice of physical postures. The Buddha, Siddharta Gautama, achieved enlightenment at the age of 35.

The Bhagavad Gita

The Gita was a conversation between Prince Arjuna and God-man Krishna and it stresses the importance of opposing evil. This is basically a conversation between Arjuna and Krishna created around 500 B.C. It also referred to as or The Song of Lord, and is currently the oldest known Yoga scripture. The Gita doesn't point to a specific time wherein yoga could have started. However, it is devoted entirely to yoga and is therefore complete confirmation that yoga has been practiced for a long time. Unfortunately, it doesn't point to a specific time wherein yoga could have started. The central theme of the Gita is that to be alive means to be active and in order to avoid difficulties in our lives and in others, our actions have to begin and have to exceed our egos

There are four core concepts from the Gita which praises the beautiful potential that exists in each one of us and, therefore in every atom of the entire cosmos, known and unknown, seen and unseen.[84]

Concept One: Look to your Dharma.

---

[84] https://dharmayogacenter.com/blog/the-four-core-concepts-from-the-bhagavad-gita/

Dharma can mean 'the law of the universe' or 'social and religious rules' and in most cases in modern yoga it is used as meaning 'one's own personal mission and purpose'

Concept Two: Absolute commitment.

Both Hinduism and Buddhism praise this fact and many books have been written about the power of focus and single-mindedness, including the Gita.

Concept Three: let the self-identity go and act out of gratitude.

In the Gita, Krishna says we our entitled to work, but not to any of the fruits of our work. What is real is the Highest Self, the Divine within us and within all life, sentient and insentient.

Concept Four: Begin the day and end the day focused on The Divine.

When life is in the flow it is so much easier. When we begin to let go of the fruits of our labor, when one is connected in every moment to the Divine it all becomes an offering. As the saying goes, 'Let go and Let God'.

In the practice of the Gita, three facets must be brought together in our modern lifestyle:

• Bhakti Yoga, the path of Divine Love or loving devotion

• Jnana Yoga, the path of knowledge or contemplation

• Karma Yoga, the path of about selfless actions.

The Gita then tried to unify these Paths of Yoga: Bhakti Yoga, Jnana Yoga, and Karma Yoga, and it is because of this that it has gained much historical importance.

The Classical Period

The Classical Period is marked by another creation – the Yoga Sutra. Written by Patanjali around the second century, it was an attempt to define and standardize Classical Yoga. It is composed of 195 aphorisms or sutras, derived from the Sanskrit word which means thread. The Sutras expound upon the Raja Yoga Path and its underlying principle, Patanjali's Eightfold path of Yoga.

To review, the Eight Limbs of Yoga are:

1. Yama, which are the social restraints or ethical values;

2. Niyama, which are the personal observances of purity, tolerance, and self study

3. <u>Asanas</u> or physical exercises;

4. Pranayama, which means breath control or regulation;

5. Pratyahara or sense withdrawal in preparation for Meditation;

6. Dharana, which is about concentration;

7. Dhyana, which means Meditation; and

8. Samadhi, which means ultimate Divine connection and complete bliss.

Patanjali wrote that each individual is both matter, our human body, called 'prakriti', and Spirit, called 'Purusha. He instructed that the two must be separated in order to cleanse the spirit – a stark contrast to Vedic and Pre-Classical Yoga that signify the union of body and spirit.

For centuries Patanjali's concept was dominant. During this time some Yogis focused exclusively on meditation and neglected their asanas. It was only later that the belief of the body as a temple was rekindled and attention to the importance of the asana was revived. This time, yogis attempted to use Yoga postures, breath and meditation together to change the body, mind and spirit.

Post Classical Yoga

At this point in the history of yoga we see a proliferation of literature on the subject, as well as the actual practice of yoga. Post-classical yoga's focus is more on the present. It no longer strives to liberate a person from reality but rather teaches one to accept it and live in the present moment.

Yoga was introduced in the West during the early 19th century. It was first studied as part of Eastern Philosophy and began as a movement for health and vegetarianism around the 1930's. By the 1960's, there was an influx of Indian teachers who expounded on Yoga. One of them was prominent Yoga Guru Swami Sivananda, as well as Maharishi Mahesh, the Yogi who popularized Transcendental Meditation. Sivananda was a doctor in Malaysia and he later opened yoga schools in America and Europe.

The most prominent of his works is his modified Five Principles of Yoga which are:

1. Savasana or proper relaxation;

2. Asanas or proper exercise;

3. Pranayama or proper breathing;

4. Proper diet; and

5. Dhyana or positive thinking and meditation

Sivananda wrote more than 200 books on Yoga and Philosophy and had many disciples who furthered the teachings of yoga. Some of them were Swami Satchitananda who is famed for introduced chanting and yoga at Woodstock; Swami Sivananada Radha who explored the connection between psychology and yoga, and Yogi Bhajan who started the teachings of Kundalini Yoga in the 70's.[85]

Up to this day, Yoga continues to grow, evolve and expand its teachings, crossing the boundaries of eastern and western culture, religion and the barrier of language.

A Deeper Look at Your Life and The Yamas and Niyamas

I suggest that as you read through the detailed overview of the precepts that follow that you take the time to meditatie on their relevance to your life. Consider your own personal experiences both past and present in reference to them. You can take almost any situation that arises in your life and consider it from the vantage point of one or more of these precepts. It can also be valuable consciously to choose a precept that you'd like to explore in depth for a month or even a year at a time investigating how the precept works in all aspects of your life. The way in which you approach the practices, and you intentions, will ultimately determine whether your practice bears fruit.

As you progress in your yoga practice, take the time to pause frequently and ask 'Who am I becoming through this practice?' and 'Am I becoming the kind of person that I would admire and want to have as my friend?'

Starting with the physical practice, asana, is often where a seed is planted, leading to deeper practices later in the yogi's journey. Those who are drawn to vigorous physical practice will, hopefully, one day find themselves drawn into the quieter, more meditative practices. As a yoga teacher it is extremely important to teach and introduce all the limbs and not to just focus on the physical. As we discussed, Sri Ramaswami and Sri Krishnamacharya have stated, by merely doing asana it is just calisthenics.

---

[85] http://www.abc-of-yoga.com/beginnersguide/yogahistory.asp

The greater focus for beginners are on the most physical or Earth rooted practices~ asana, breath work (pranayama) and meditation. These form an embodied approach to spiritual practice, where we use the body and all our sensual capacities in the service of regeneration and transformation. This is contrasted to many approaches in which the body is seen as an obstacle that must be transcended. The core principles for living are the yamas and niyamas. These restraints and observances are the principles that form the central vein from which all other yoga practices spring.

There are many branches to the tree of yoga, from devotion to intellect, from service to physical purification. Patanjali's Yoga Sutras, clearly define an eight-limbed path called ashtanga. This path creates the framework for whatever path we choose to take on our journey. Let's look at these principles in depth.

The Ten Living Principles

The first limb, the yamas, consisting of characteristics observed since the beginning of time as being central to any life lived in freedom. They are mostly concerned with how we use our energy in relationship to others and in a subtler sense, our relationship to ourselves. The sages recognized that stealing from your neighbor was likely to cause disruption, lying to your wife would cause suffering, and violence begets more violence. The results of living by these observances are conducive to living a peaceful life.

The second limb, the niyamas, constitutes a 'code for living'. It fosters the soulfulness of the individual and has to do with the choices we make. The yamas and niyamas are emphatic descriptions of who we are when we are connected to our Source. Rather than a list of do's and don'ts, they tell us that our fundamental nature is compassionate, generous, honest, and peaceful.

What yoga teaches us is that who we are and how we are made up is the ultimate proof of a life lived in freedom in the Truth. The yamas and niyamas ask us to remember is that the practice, the asana, the techniques and forms are not goals in themselves but simply vehicles for getting to the essence of who we are!

Yamas~ Wise Characteristics

Ahimsa~ Compassion for All Living Things!

Ahimsa is usually translated as nonviolence. Firstly, we have to learn how to be nonviolent toward ourselves. If we were able to play back the often unkind, unhelpful, and destructive comments and judgments silently made toward our self in any given day, this may give us some idea of the enormity of the challenge of self-acceptance and self worth. If we were to speak these thoughts out loud to another person, even to someone we care little about we would realize how truly devastating violence to the self can be!

In truth, few of us would dare to be as unkind to others as we are to ourselves. This can be as subtle as the criticism of our body when we look in the mirror in the morning, or when we denigrate our best efforts. Any thought, word, or action that prevents ourselves or someone else from growing and living freely is one that is harmful.

Extending this compassion to all living creatures is the recognition that the streams and rivers of the earth are no different from the blood coursing through our arteries. In this place of compassion we naturally find ourselves wanting to protect all living things.

In contrast, when we accept and allow our feelings of anger, jealousy, or rage rather than see them as signs of our spiritual failure, we can begin to learn the root causes of these feelings learn from them and move past them. By getting real with ourselves and truly recognizing our own violent tendencies we can begin to understand them. We can and will, with practice, learn to contain these energies for our own well-being and for the protection of others. All humans and sentient beings share the desire to be loved. To come to this deeper truth we must do the tough work of facing our shadow self.

My first mantra was learned through Amma, the hugging saint, right after my mom died. She showed me Divine Maternal Love and I am forever grateful for her soulful look and much needed long motherly hug. That night I learned the mantra, which would be with me always, 'Om Lokah Samastah Sukhino Bhavantu'. This mantra is a beautiful and very powerful tool to experience this concept.

In considering ahimsa ask, am I living with my life in continuity of the meaning of the mantra, 'May all beings be happy, healthy and free and may my right actions contribute to that happiness.'

Satya~ Commitment to the Truth.

This precept is based on the concept of being impeccable to our word. This means that when we say something, we are sure of its truth. Satya is about understanding that honest communication and action form the foundation of any healthy relationship and mistruths, white lies or falsification of any kind harm ourselves and others. If we were to follow this precept with commitment, many of us would have a great deal less to say each day! Gossip is the worst form of this miscommunication. Take a stand and speak out against this misuse of language! Use your 5th Chakra!

Commitment to the truth isn't always easy, but with practice true communication allows us to begin taking care of little matters before they become big ones.

Probably the hardest form of this practice is being true to our own heart and inner destiny, we may lack the courage and conviction to live our truth. Following what we know to be essential for our growth may mean leaving unhealthy relationships or jobs and taking risks that jeopardize our own comfortable position. The truth is rarely convenient. While our choices may not be easy, at the end of the day we know we are in Satya when we truly feel at peace.

Asteya~ Non Stealing.

Asteya arises out of the understanding that all misappropriation is an expression of a feeling of lack, or not living in Abundance. What really matters is our health, the richness of our inner life and the joy and love we are able to give and receive from others. Embrace living in Abundance!

The practice of asteya asks us to be careful not to take anything that has not been freely given. This can be as subtle as inquiring whether someone is free to speak with us on the phone (ie: telemarketers/phone calls without appointments) or before we launch into a tirade about our problems. Or reserving our questions after a class for another time, rather than hoarding a teacher's attention long after the official class time has ended. In taking someone's time that may not have been freely given, we are, in effect, stealing.

Not stealing demands that we cultivate a certain level of self-sufficiency so that we do not demand more of others, our family, or our community than we need. It means that we don't take any more than we need, because that would be taking from others. A helpful way of practicing asteya when you find yourself dwelling on the 'not enough' of life is to ask, 'How is this grasping attitude preventing me from finding joy in the things that I already have?'

226

Another way of fostering this sense of abundance is to take a moment before going to sleep to find a place of gratitude. This can be as simple as the gift of having a loving partner, a favorite pet, the blessing of having optimal health, or the pleasure of spending time in the garden. Begin a gratitude practice!

Aparigraha--Non Grasping.

Holding on to things and being free are two different feelings entirely. The ordinary 'ego' mind is constantly manipulating our view on reality, building up more and more validation of how things are and how others 'are'. This is the ego mind's way of generating confidence and security in its beliefs. It creates self-images, constructs concepts and paradigms that all feed its wn false sense of certainty. Sadly, unenlightened or 'not awakened' people then defend this colored perspective by unconsciously shaping every situation to reinforce that false certainty.

The resistance to change, and tenaciously holding on to things, causes great suffering. The one rule that we can count on in this life is:. Change is the only constant.

We all have at one point tried to hold on too tightly to anything, whether it be possessiveness of our youthful girlfriend or boyfriend, our youth, our career identity, the list goes on and on. This behavior has only led to the destruction of those very things we most value. Our best bet lies in taking down our walls, opening our heart and allowing ourselves to grow.

The practice of aparigraha also requires that we look at the way we use material things to reinforce our sense of identity or our roles. The executive ego loves to recruit external objects; the right clothes, the car, house, job, or social status to maintain this 'illusion'. Although the practice of not grasping may first begin as intentionally withdrawing from reaching for external things, eventually the need to reach outward at all diminishes. Once there is a real recognition of that the Truth has always been and always is available to us, it is within that connection that we ultimately find our true growth and potential in this life.

Brahmacharya; Merging with Oneness

Brahmacharya means literally merging one's energy with Source. It is commonly mis-translated as celibacy, it is really about the dilemma of how to use sexual energy wisely. Practicing brahmacharya means that we use our sexual energy to regenerate our connection to our Spiritual Self. It also means that we don't use this energy in any way that might harm another.

It may be easier to understand brahmacharya if we remove the sexual designation and look at it purely as Divine Energy. Of course, when any energy is sublimated or suppressed, it has the tendency to backfire, expressing itself in negative ways. Ultimately it is not a matter of whether we use our sexual energy but how we use it.

In looking at your own relationship to sexual energy, consider whether the ways you express that energy bring you closer to or farther away from your spiritual self.

Niyamas~ The Codes for Living with Embodiment of Spirit

Soucha~ Purity.

Soucha also spelled Shaucha, is about living purely, and maintaining cleanliness in body, mind, and environment so that we can bring ourselves to a higher vibration. For instance, when are intentional about eating healthy, clean food, untainted by pesticides and unnatural additives, the body starts to function more smoothly. When we read books that elevate our consciousness, see movies that inspire, and associate with uplifting people, we are feeding the mind in a way that nourishes our own peace. By creating a home environment that is elegant, simple, and uncluttered this generates an atmosphere where we are not constantly distracted.

Its meaning is 'that and nothing else' This involves about clearly discerning and making choices about what you want and don't want in your life, and only allowing in what you DO want. The practice of shaucha allows you to experience life more vividly. A clean pallate enjoys the sweetness of an apple and the taste of pure water; a clear mind can appreciate the beauty of poetry and the wisdom imparted in a story; a polished table reveals the deep grain of the wood. This practice both generates beauty and allows us to appreciate it in all its many forms.[86]

Santosha~ Contentment.

BE HERE NOW.

~Ram Dass

Santosha, is the ability to feel satisfied within the container of one's immediate experience.

---

[86]

Contentment shouldn't be confused with happiness or complacency. We can be in difficult, even painful circumstances and still find some semblance of contentment. 'When you rest you rust', as the old saying goes. Santosha it is a sign that we are at peace with whatever stage of growth we are in and the circumstances we find ourselves in.

Contentment is about acceptance of the NOW moment, as well as creating space for hopefulness. The ability to sustain one's spirits even in dire situations, is proof that of this ultimate place of finding one's central sense of balance. [87]

Tapas~ Burning Enthusiasm!

For what greater purpose do we need tapas, or discipline?

Pema Chodron, the author of many books on Tibetan Buddhism

Literally translated as "fire" or "heat," tapas is the disciplined use of our energy, as in burning enthusiasm. Tapas is a way of directing our energy like a focused beam of light cutting through the dark. Tapas keeps us on track so that we don't waste our time and energy on superfluous or trivial matters. When this energy is strong, so also are the processes of transmutation and metamorphism.

Ayurveda is a wonderful partnership to this study, it is the sister science of Yoga. This science of Medicine teaches us to regulate fire in the body through food and lifestyle practices.

Music is also a wonderful tool to increase your internal passion.

---

[87] Donna Farhi, Yoga Mind, Body & Spirit: A Return to Wholeness

Swadhyaya~ Self-Study.

Sustain the heart fire.

~ Shiva Rea

Any activity that cultivates self-reflective consciousness can be considered swadhyaya. The soul is enlightened by the activities that will best illuminate it. This varies from person to person. Someone may be drawn to write, while another will discover herself through painting or athletics. Another person may come to know himself through mastering an instrument, or through service at local charity. Still another may learn hidden aspects of herself through the practice of meditation.

The form that this self-study takes is different for everyone. Whatever the practice, as long as there is an true intention to know yourself through it, and the commitment to see the process through, almost any activity can become an opportunity for learning about yourself. Swadhyaya means staying with our process through thick and thin because it's usually when the going gets rough that we have the greatest opportunity to learn about ourselves.

Ishvara Pranidhana~ Celebration of the Spirit!

Life is not truly meaningful unless we make meaning happen through the attention and care we express through our actions. Setting intention is what sets the Spiritual Sadhana of daily life from the mundane. We can find this celebration of Spirit in simple acts; when we set a table with beauty, when we light a candle before practicing, when we remove our shoes before entering a sacred space, when we look at a flower.

Life can become Celebration!!! Yoga tells us that the spiritual is everything; we simply need to notice the extraordinary omnipresence that dwells in all things. By putting aside some time each day, we can begin to practice surrender. This is a simple practice of daily, intentionally tapping into something greater our selves, the Highest Self. This might take the form of being out in your garden, enjoying the dawn or a sunset, breathing slowly to clear your mind, or engaging in a more formal practice such as reading a spiritual text, a moon cycle ritual, prayer, meditation or a mantra practice.

This practice requires that we have recognized that there is some omnipresent force larger than ourselves that is guiding and directing the course of our lives. We all have had the experience of looking back at some event in our life that at the time may have seemed so painful, extremely chaotic, confusing, and disruptive or in a place of sadness and grief. Later, in hindsight, these events come to make perfect sense in the context of our personal destiny. We recognize that that change that occurred during that time was necessary for our growth, and that we are happier and better for it.

Look for the serendipitous moments! When we surrender to the Flow we begin to recognize every Divine coincidence. There are no accidents!!! Chance meetings all have some greater significance in the larger scheme of our destiny! When we are the master of our universe, it's hard to trust anything but your own self-made, heavy-handed and forced plans.

Ishvarapranidhana asks us to take that step forward, without fully knowing the outcome. To step out in pure Faith! This is a true practice and all the limbs of yoga lead us here. The time is now to step through that door, onto a clearn and unseen step, the first one on an invisible staircase leading us to our Ultimate Destiny!

This is a mantra that has been helpful on so many occasions. The steps appear only when we have FAITH to step with all our weight, no holding back even an ounce! The crystal staircase will appear with our Faith! This is what makes each day an adventure! It makes our life appear like a wild mustang horse racing into the unknown, just for the joy of the ability to run free!

Ultimately, Ishvarapranidhana means surrendering our personal will to the Divine Intelligence, so that we can fulfill our destiny. By setting aside daily time to get quiet and clear, we can begin to differentiate between the cluttered thoughts of our ordinary ego-mind and hear the Divine Wisdom that comes through as intuition. We start to embody the mystery of life. We listen with PRESENCE. Everything and anything becomes a sign of this Oneness. Check in, tap in and connect!

Chapter 11

Yoga Anatomy 101 and Our Immune System

An asana, or yoga pose, is a container for an experience. An asana is not an exercise for strengthening or stretching a particular muscle or muscle group, although it might have that effect.

~Leslie Kaminoff, Yoga Anatomy-2nd Edition

In this next chapter we will swith gears to discuss the basic systems of the body in relation to a yoga practice or teaching a yoga class. The human body is extremely complex and therefore this serves as an overview for you to utilize to obtain a foundational knowledge of how to safely move the body when practicing yoga. One of my mentors and teachers, Judith Lastier, wrote to me in an inscription of a book to continue to always study anatomy! I have taken those words of wisdom to heart and have really enjoyed the journey. I encourage you to do the same!

Systems of the Human Body

There are 12 systems in the human body: A group of Systems composes an Organism, such as the human body[88].

- Circulatory
- Integumentary system
- Skeletal system
- Reproductive system
- Digestive system
- Endocannabinoid system

---

[88] http://en.wikipedia.org/wiki/Human_physiology#Systems

- Excretory/ Urinary system

- Respiratory system

- Endocrine system

- Immune/ Lymphatic system

- Muscular system

- Nervous system

Let's look into the twelve Systems of the Human Body a little closer: These specific systems are widely studied in Human anatomy. 'Human' systems are also present in many other animals.

1. Circulatory system: pumping and channeling blood to and from the body and lungs with heart, blood and blood vessels.

2. Integumentary system: skin, hair, fat, and nails.

3. Skeletal system: structural support and protection with bones, cartilage, ligaments and tendons.

4. Reproductive system: the sex organs, such as ovaries, fallopian tubes, uterus, vagina, mammary glands, testes, vas deferens, seminal vesicles and prostate

5. Digestive system: digestion and processing food with salivary glands, esophagus, stomach, liver, gallbladder, pancreas, intestines, rectum and anus.

6. Endocannabinoid system: neuro-modulatory lipids and receptors involved in a variety of physiological processes including immune function appetite, pain-sensation, mood, motor learning, synaptic plasticity, and memory.

7. Excretory/ Urinary system: kidneys, ureters, bladder and urethra involved in fluid balance, electrolyte balance and excretion of urine.

8. Respiratory system: the organs used for breathing, the pharynx, larynx, bunghole, bronchi, lungs and diaphragm.

9. Endocrine system: communication within the body using hormones made by endocrine glands such as the hypothalamus, pituitary gland, pineal body or pineal gland, thyroid, parathyroids and adrenals, i.e., adrenal glands.

10. Immune/ Lymphatic system: structures involved in the transfer of lymph between tissues and the blood stream; includes the lymph and the nodes and vessels.

11. Muscular system: allows for manipulation of the environment, provides locomotion, maintains posture, and produces heat. Includes only skeletal muscle, not smooth muscle or cardiac muscle.

12. Nervous system: collecting, transferring and processing information with brain, spinal cord and peripheral nervous system.[89]

There is a little difference between the male and female skeleton, but mostly they look similar. The female skeleton is slightly smaller and less robust. The female skeleton also has a wider pelvis, compared to the male skeletal system. So study the above diagram, and for memorizing, draw it a few times and keep labeling!

A basic human skeleton is studied in schools with a simple diagram. It is also studied in art schools, while in-depth study of the skeleton is done in the medical field. Next we will look at the bone structure of the human body learn and a simple technique to memorize the names of all the bones.

---

[89] http://inaa.dvrlists.com/systems-of-the-body/

Fun Facts About the Skeleton

Given above were the tips on memorizing the various parts of the skeleton. Here are some interesting facts about skeleton.

- Among the 206 bone in the human skeletal system
- An infant skeleton has 350 bones, and some of these bones fuse.
- Did you know that half of these 206 bones are present in the hands and feet?
- 52 of them are found in our feet!
- Bones are made of hard stuff which makes them strong, however, bones also have many living cells that help in their growth and repair.
- Did you know that the smallest bone in the human body is located in the ear? The size of the smallest bone called stirrup, is the size of a grain of rice.
- Bones are filled with bone marrow, which is a fatty substance.
- To keep the bones strong, one should exercise regularly.
- In adults, the bones contribute to 14% of the total body weight.
- Did you know that one person out of 20 has an extra rib? Super strange!
- The cartilage disintegrates faster than the bone, therefore you will observe the absence of nose or ears in the skeleton.
- Babies don't have kneecaps. Technically, they do have kneecaps but they are soft cartilage and yet to harden into bones.
- Giraffes and humans both have 8 bones in their neck, however the vertebrae present in the giraffe's neck are way longer!
- Bones are stronger than concrete and steel, yet doctors can be seen fixing fractures year-round. [90]

---

[90] http://www.buzzle.com/articles/labeled-skeletal-system-diagram.html

The skeletal system is one of the important human body systems. We will divide the human skeletal system into 4 sections for better understanding, so let's start from top to bottom and study the human skeleton!

Bone Structure of the Head and Skull

The head consists of many bones, mainly the cranium, jaw bones (maxilla and mandible) and the facial bones. There are many bones which comprise the skeletal system and one of the important one is the cranium, which is commonly called skull. It protects the brain from any accidents or injury, it acts like a framework of the head. The mandible is the strongest among the bones of the head.

Bone Structure of the Chest and Hip

The bones shown in the chest and hip region in the labeled human skeleton diagram are the ribs, vertebrae, pelvis, OS coxae, sacrum and coccyx. Total there are 12 pairs of ribs, as you can see in the diagram. The last pair of the ribs, which is at the bottom of the rib, are called floating ribs, as they are not attached to the sternum. The ribs are arranged in a cage-like structure which protects vital organs like the heart and lungs. In the back area, the bones that protect the spinal column are called vertebrae. They help to protect the spinal cord in the body. Pelvis is a Latin word, which means 'basin', it is also known as hip girdle. The primary function of the pelvis is to bear the weight of the upper body.

Bone Structure of the Hand

There are around 7 major bones from the shoulder to the palms. They are scapula, humerus, radius, ulna, carpels, metacarpals, and phalanges. The scapulae is the triangular, wing-shaped bones, which are located on the

238

shoulders. Humerus is located in the upper arm. The radius and ulna together constitute the forearm. Carpals are the bones which form wrist. These are attached to metacarpals which are joined to phalanges

Bone Structure of the Leg

The bone structure in the leg is easy to memorize and draw, as it consists mainly of 6 bones. These bones are femur, patella, tibia, fibula, tarsals, and metatarsals. Femur is the longest and heaviest bone in the body, and helps to support the weight of the body. Patella is located in front of the knee-joint, and commonly called the kneecap. It helps to cover and protect the knee-joint. Fibula and tibia bones are located in the calves of the legs. The foot bones shown in the labeled diagram of skeletal system, are the tarsals and the metatarsals. There are seven tarsal bones, which are followed by metatarsals which are then followed by phalanges or toe bones.

Memorizing Bone Names, Skeleton Anatomy

The skeleton is divided into two categories: the axial skeleton and the appendicular skeleton.

The axial skeleton consists of the core, including your skull, vertebrae, ribs. It forms the axis on which all the other bones attach.

Rather than memorizing all the bones of the appendicular skeleton, it easier to remember what the axial skeleton contains and know that everything else is appendicular.[91]

It can be a bit difficult to remember all the scientific names of bones, but here is a great technique of remembering the names. First, divide the labeled diagram of skeleton in 4 sections, like above, which are head, arms, chest + hips and the fourth one - legs.

---

[91] https://differentmedicalcareers.com/easy-way-to-learn-the-bones-of-the-body-tips-and-songs/

For the head remember:

J, F and C: Jaw bones, Facial bones and Cranium.

For legs remember:

F, P, T, F, T and M and memorize the order, these letters stand for Femur, Patella, Tibia, Fibula, Tarsals and Metatarsals. In a similar manner use the method, for chest + hips section and hands section

Fundamental Muscle Anatomy

Have you ever thougth about the how important our muscles really are, and truly been in a place of gratitude for our musclar system? Every single movement in our body is carried out by a muscular pulling or contracting. About half of our body's weight is muscle.

While the skeletal system is responsible for giving the human body a frame, the muscular system then adds to the frame through mechanisms of support. Muscle hold the skeletal system in place while also allowing it the movement necessary to create human posture, motion, and activity from the basic of sitting and standing to the finest intricate motions such as athleticism to the finest motor skill manipulation. Muscle tissue continuously gives the skeletal system this support even at rest. The human body in the sitting position is then using muscle activity to hold the head upright, to balance on the buttocks, and to keep appendages in a place of rest.[92]

In the muscular system, muscle tissue is categorized into three distinct types: skeletal, cardiac, and smooth. Each type of muscle tissue in the human body has a unique structure and a very specific role. Skeletal muscle moves bones and other structures. Cardiac muscle contracts the heart to pump blood.

---

[92] http://muscularsystem.organsofthebody.com

The smooth muscle tissue that forms organs like the stomach and bladder changes shape to facilitate bodily functions.[93]

The collective mass of all the organs associated with the muscular system roughly accounts for almost half of your body weight. Science has identified and named hundreds of muscles in the human body. All the varities of movements in the body can be grouped into two categories, voluntary movements and involuntary movements.

Muscles play a significant role in the body's ability to maintain a constant temperature regardless of the temperature which surrounds it. Metabolism is the process of turning food into energy. Merabolism releases heat, which in turn helps to maintain a regulated body temperature. Muscles, comprise approximately 40% of the body's weight, and carry enough impact on the human body based solely on their mass to be the prime source of the body's ability to heat itself and maintain a steady constant temperature. To regulate the body's ability to increase and decrease of temperature the different type of muscle fibers have different roles. The chronic muscle fiber activity maintains body temperature and the strenuous muscular activity increases body temperature, encouraging the human body to produce sweat to cool the temperature.

Skeletal Muscle Structure Overview

We will take a look at the structure and the anatomical study of the microscopic structure of normal adult skeletal muscle and addresses The purpose here is to serve as a reference for you in understanding basic muscle function and structure.

---

[93] https://www.visiblebody.com/learn/muscular/muscle-types

Basic structure and terminology

A layer of dense connective tissue, which is known as 'epimysium' and is continuous with the tendon, surrounds each muscle. A muscle is composed of numerous bundles of muscle fibers, termed 'fascicles', which are separated from each other by a connective tissue layer termed 'perimysium'. Endomysium is the connective tissue that separates individual muscle fibers from each other. Mature muscle cells are termed muscle fibers or 'myofibers'. Each myofiber is a 'multinucleate syncytium' formed by fusion of immature muscle cells termed 'myoblasts'.[94]

Basic constituents of skeletal muscle

Sarcoplasm, the cytoplasm of each myofiber, is occupied largely by the contractile apparatus of the cell. This is composed of myofibrils arranged in sarcomeres, which are the contractile units of the cell. The sarcomeres contain a number of proteins, including alpha actinin, which is the major constituent of the Z band. The Z band is a dark thin protein band to which actin filaments are attached in a striated muscle fiber, marking the boundaries between adjacent sarcomeres[95] and actin and myosin, which are the major components of the thin and thick filaments.

The remainder of the sarcoplasm, located between the myofibrils, is termed the 'intermyofibrillar network' and contains the mitochondria, lipid, glycogen, T-tubules, and sarcoplasmic reticulum. T-tubules and sarcoplasmic reticulum are responsible for conduction of electrical signals from the cell surface and the intracellular storage and release of calcium required for contraction to occur.[96]

---

[94] http://emedicine.medscape.com/article/1923188-overview
[95] http://www.dictionary.com/browse/z-line
[96] http://www.teachpe.com/anatomy/structure_skeletal_muscle.php

Love Your Lymph

Half of your lymphatics are actually around your digestive tract and work to maintain proper immune response to whatever is in your gut. Constipation in your digestive tract causes a back up in your internal lymphatics, as there is no place for new trash to flow.

~ Dr. Byron Richards, BCCN

The healthier your lymph system is the healthier you will be and and it will Love You Back! The benefits for being mindful of your lymph system are profound. Your body can respond faster to invading infection, as the lymph is where T-cells are found. The T-cells help identify invaders and support the body's natural immune system.

Another way the lymph helps aid in immunity is through a special type of cell called the endothelial cell. Endothelial cells line your digestive tract and can actually sense the type of bacteria that are present in your digestive tract. Using this perception, instructions are then given to form lymph tissue that is specific to keeping that particular foreign type of cell in check. This helps provide protection from viruses. If this system gets out of balance our digestive system is more prone to become a friendly host for pathogenic bacteria such as Candida and h. pylori. The health of our GUT impacts overall health![97]

The Lymphatic System and Gut Health

Most people have very little understanding of where the lymph system is or how the lymph system functions. To expain, the lymph system actually runs throughout our bodies and plays a vital role in sweeping toxins away. It

---

[97] http://nourishholisticnutrition.com/lymph-flowing-river-of-life/

actually acts as a filter and ensures that our immune system stays strong. The lymph also helps with the absorption and transport of fats.

Our lymphatic system is basically our body's cleansing system, waste removal. Although it has millions of vessels just like the blood system, it has no strong heart to keep lymph moving. Instead, lymph is moved by simple muscle action such as breathing, walking, intestinal activity and so on. As muscles tighten, lymph vessels are squeezed and lymph is pushed along and filtered through lymph nodes on its way back to the veins and the heart. We need to keep lymph moving efficiently and one way is through yoga!

The lymph requires very little pressure to help it along, and in lymph drainage, a modality in healing that focuses on the lymph, the pressure of only the weight of a nickel is necessary! Thekey is that we apply this movement and pressure every day, regularly, and do not let the lymph coagulate. One technique for moving lymph was developed by Donna Eden, and is called Energy Medicine. I encourage you to look it up! It is a fun practice to include into your Daily Sadhana, and self care routine.

The next question is, 'do I have stagnant lymph?' Lymph circulation, as mentioned, relies on body motion and muscle contraction. This is why it's common for inactive people to experience pain between the shoulder blades, edema, headaches at the base of the neck, snoring/sleep apnea. Inactivity also causes hands or arms falling asleep, to have frequent earaches and congestion or a sense of overall fatigue.

Gut health is extremely vital to lymph function and internal lymph flow, and vice versa. Lymph trash flows into a major vein, and then to your liver for processing, then mostly through your gallbladder, into your gut, and out. A problem anywhere along this functional lineup of trash handlers causes a rebound effect, like dominoes falling in the wrong direction."

Lymph System 101

How does the lymph system work? The lymph system is the body's drainage system. It is composed of a network of vessels and small structures called lymph nodes. The lymph vessels convey excess fluid collected from all over the body back into the blood circulation. Along the way, however, these fluids are forced to percolate through the lymph nodes so that they can be filtered. Harmful organisms are trapped and destroyed by the specialized white blood cells, called 'lymphocytes', that are present in these nodes. Lymphocytes are also added to the lymph that flows out of nodes and back to the bloodstream.[98]

Antibodies are specialized proteins that are manufactured by the lymph system. The body produces in response to invasion by a foreign substance. The process begins when an antigen stimulates specialized lymphocytes into action, called 'B cells. Antibodies then counteract invading antigens by combining with the antigen to render it harmless to the body.

Certain antibodies coat the harmful organisms so that the body's scavenger cells can recognize and destroy them more easily. The antibody molecule combines with the antigen molecule by matching combining sites; they fit together like the pieces of a jigsaw puzzle. Other antibodies that neutralize toxins produced by bacteria are called 'antitoxins'.

When the lymph is in a period of active antibody production, the nodes often enlarge and become tender to the touch.[99]

During the course of infection, cells that have identified an invader, such as the dendritic cells of your front line immune, must migrate into your

---

[98] http://www.wellnessresources.com/health/articles/a_healthy_lymph_system_is_vital_for_flu_fighting_immunity/

[99] https://health.howstuffworks.com/human-body/systems/lymphatic/lymph-system.htm

lymphatic system and present their findings to a subgroup of lymphocytes called T helper cells that reside within lymph tissue.

T helper cells have various meeting rooms within the lymph nodes and lymph tissue where they 'discuss' the problem and refine their identification of the invader.Once T helper cells reach consensus, they present the identification tag of the invader, the antigen, to the higher powered immune system, so that it is identified in the body. The fighters resting in the lymph tissue then spring into action, having specific knowledge of the enemy's appearance. At the same time, the call goes out to manufacture more immune troops, requiring your liver to send protein. This runs smoothly ONLY if your system is adequate in many basic nutrients.

How to Improve Lymph Flow

- Any exercise will get the lymph flowing but exercises that have a slight bounce to them work the best. Walking, running, or any sport where you do these is good.

- If you have a min-trampoline (re-bounder) you can gently bounce on that for five or ten minutes a day.

- If you do not have a re-bounder you can simply bounce by lifting your heals off the ground and then back down as you stand with your arms at your side.

- Deep belly breathing and stretching through yoga, tai chi and qi gong are all excellent ways to get the lymph flowing again.

- You can also do self-lymph massage by gently using your fingertips, using a soft gentle touch. Use palms for larger areas. This is not like a massage, it is very subtle.

- You can also work with a specialist Lymph Drainage. This is especially helpful to those with cancer and autoimmune dis-ease.

- Dry brushing the skin using a special natural bristle brush also helps get lymph moving. Start with the legs or arms and sweep towards the heart. This is a great action to add to your daily Sadhana or self care routine.
- To help relieve congestion; try gently tapping. You can start alongside your nasal passages, under your cheek bones, around the eyes, behind the ears, under the jaw and down the neck moving to just under the collar bone.
- Be sure to drink plenty of filtered water, at least ½ oz. per pound of bodyweight a day!

Foods and Nutrients to Support Lymph and Immunity

All foods and nutrients that help support gallbladder, liver and improve digestive health will support the lymph. All foods that are rich in antioxidants and phytonutrients are also excellent.

- Phytonutrients only come from plants.
- We need 9-13 fist sized servings a day of clean, organic, non GMO produce.
- Athletes and active people need 13-18 plant powered food servings A DAY!
- The ORAC value determines the amount of antioxidants that are present in the plant. A great reference tool for this is a super simple food rating system called NutriPoints by Dr. Roy Vartebedian. No more counting calories, protein, carbs, fats, cholesterol, sodium, sugar, vitamins, minerals…all that work has been done for you, and put into one number—the Nutripoint score. The higher the score, the

higher its nutritional value, based on nutrient density. .[100] I highly recommend his books, CD and website.

- Free radicals are present in the body for a number of reasons including eating fried foods, drinking alcohol, tobacco smoke, pesticides, air pollutants; the list goes on and on.

- Even vigorous exercise produces free radicals with oxidative stresses placed on the body.

- Free radicals can cause damage to parts of cells such as proteins, DNA, and cell membranes by stealing their electrons through a process called oxidation.[101]

- The antioxidants present in the body are what balance out free radicals.

- When free radicals are not stabilized dis-ease will surely develop.

21 Days to Feeling Fit Guide Book + Boosting our Immune

I have a great tool for you, and it is free. It is my *21 Days to Feeling Fit Guide Book*[102] that includes the details of a simple cranberry cleanse and Shred 10 program[103] with whole food recipes, smoothies and a fun intention setting and tracking process. You can download the free eBook on my website online store at www.yoga4love.com and begin tomorrow! The cranberry cleanse in the eBook is an eleven day free cleanse that is great for building up gut health and eliminating berrer, all of which is essential to an overall healthy immune. It is followed by a short detx of unhealthy habits called a Shred 10. This can be done on your own or with an accountability group! Detoxing is not only food, but replacing unhealthy habits with simple

---

[100] http://nutripoints.com/
[101] google
[102] www.yoga4love.com
[103] www.shred10.com

changes such as getting 7.7 to 9 hours of sleep nightly, drinking ½ z. of pure water per pound of body weight, eating clean and exercizing for at least twenty minutes minimum four times a week.

Here are some additional ways you can get started on building up your immunity:

- Drink pure warm water with fresh organic lemons (with the rind) or a couple drops of lemon essential oil (therapeutic grade) added. My husband gave up his morning coffee several years ago simply to starting his day by drinking this, along with eating the Juice Plus chewables.

- Make a cranberry detox drink with fresh lemon juice, Apple Cider Vinegar and pure cranberry, the kind you get in a glass jar and have to shake up. I began doing this several months ago as son as I wake as a daily routine before I break my fast with a Juice Plus complete smoothie made into a hot latte or a hot chai. I have been the most regular I have ever been in my life, as my gut health has flourshed!

- Eat leafy greens and green foods like chlorella and spirulina.

- Eat fresh organic blueberries, blackberries and organic strawberries.

- Get whole food essential fatty acids in daily by etaing ground flax seed, hemp seeds and chia seeds.

Other Helpful Nutrients

- Whole food enzymes, especially the Proteolytic enzyme Bromelain (found in pineapple core) and papain (found in papaya, whole fruit) are amazing anti-inflammatory nutrients.

- Quercetin acts as an anti-histamine and anti-inflammatory. It is found in deep, dark red and purple fruits: Red grapes, currents, blueberries, red apples, acerola cherries, blackberries.

○ Many essential oils have antimicrobial properties like Oregano oil. Make sure to only use therapeutic pharmaceutical grade oils.

Exercises to Help Drain Your Lymphatic System

Reflex Point Stimulation

There is a reflex point that helps stimulate lymphatic drainage in the upper body. It is located at the bottom of the breastbone, or sternum. Vigorously rub this area for about two minutes to help the lymphatic drainage.

Lymph Drainage

You can help lymph nodes drain and flow by gently rubbing or milking. You always want to do this toward the heart. This works quite well with sore throats or sinus congestion. Use an Ayurvedic oil or massage oil and start under the jaw. Work down the throat on each side of the large muscle on both sides of the neck. !

Move to the base of the skull with your thumbs just behind the ears. Push under the skull, into the neck, with firm pressure slowly going toward the collar bone. Continue to do this, and each time move the thumbs closer together toward the spine.[104]

Axillary Traction

One other important and easy technique is called axillary traction, meaning 'armpit pull.' Lie on your back and have someone stand at your head, have them lift you by grasping you under your armpits. Then they gently and firmly pull you up and back with your arms relaxed by your sides

---

[104] https://www.drdavidwilliams.com/lymphatic-system-drainage-exercises/#top

until. Your partner should maintain this traction lift, for 20 to 30 seconds. After a short rest, repeat the procedure four to five times.

Endocrine System Overview

The endocrine system is the other communication system in the body made up of endocrine glands that produce hormones. The hormones are chemical substances released into the bloodstream to guide such processes as metabolism, growth, and sexual development. Hormones are also involved in regulating our emotional life.[105]

Thyroid gland

The thyroid gland secretes thyroxin, a hormone that can reduce concentration and lead to irritability when the thyroid is overactive and cause drowsiness and a sluggish metabolism when the thyroid is underactive.

Parathyroid glands

Near the thyroid are 4 tiny pea-shaped organs, the parathyroids, that secrete parathormone to control and balance the levels of calcium and phosphate in the blood and tissue fluids. This, in turn, affects the excitability of the nervous system.

Pineal gland

The pineal gland is a pea-sized gland that apparently responds to exposure to light and regulates activity levels over the course of the day.The Pineal gland activation is also directly related to your connection to higher consciousness and plays an important role in reaching the highest Self.

---

[105] https://emedicine.medscape.com/

*NOTE Floride hardens or calcifies the pineal and is a know toxin to the human body, as well.

The pineal gland has been linked to extrasensory abilities; among them intuition, discernment, psychic awareness and expanded mind capacity. The gland's semblance to the human eye and its location in the brain make it appear to be, quite literally, *the mind's eye*. Practically speaking, the desires of our heart direct our eyes to and from that which we do and don't want. The eyes then receive light into the body, send it to the brain, which transports it to the pineal gland. The light stimulus activates the gland.

Calcification is the biggest problem for the pineal gland. Fluoride accumulates in the pineal gland more than any other organ and leads to the formation of phosphate crystals. As your pineal gland hardens due to the crystal production, less melatonin is produced and regulation of your wake-sleep cycle gets disturbed.

In addition to fluoride, halides like chlorine and bromine also accumulate and damage the pineal gland. Eliminating fluoride may be the best first step for reducing health concerns. Use fluoride-free toothpaste, avoid tap water, and drink filtered water. For the best filtered water, use a reverse osmosis water filter or a gravity fed system certified and tested to remove at least 97% of fluoride.[106]

Pancreas

The pancreas lies in the curve of the duodenum and controls the level of sugar in the blood by secreting insulin and glucagon.

Pituitary gland

---

[106] https://www.mbsfestival.com.au/healthy-living-hub/fluoride-third-eye/

The pituitary gland produces the largest number of different hormones and, therefore, has the widest range of effects on the body's functions. The posterior pituitary is controlled by the nervous system. It produces 2 hormones: vasopressin, which causes blood pressure to rise and regulates the amount of water in the body's cells, and oxytocin, which causes the uterus to contract during childbirth and lactation to begin. The anterior pituitary, often called the "master gland," responds to chemical messages from the bloodstream to produce numerous hormones that trigger the action of other endocrine glands disturbed

Hormones are chemical messengers created by the body. They transfer information from one set of cells to another to coordinate the functions of different parts of the body.

The major glands of the endocrine system are the:

- Hypothalamus
- Pituitary
- Thyroid
- Parathyroids
- Adrenals
- pineal body
- reproductive organs; ovaries and testes
- The pancreas is also a part of this system; it has a role in hormone production, as well as in digestion.

The endocrine system is regulated by feedback in much the same way that a thermostat regulates the temperature in a room. For the hormones that are regulated by the pituitary gland, a signal is sent from the hypothalamus to the pituitary gland in the form of a 'releasing hormone,' which stimulates the pituitary to secrete a 'stimulating hormon'" into the circulation.

The stimulating hormone then signals the target gland to secrete its hormone. As the level of this hormone rises in the circulation, the hypothalamus and the pituitary gland shut down secretion of the releasing hormone and the stimulating hormone, which in turn slows the secretion by the target gland. This system results in stable blood concentrations of the hormones that are regulated by the pituitary gland.

Gonads

These reproductive glands, the testes in males and the ovaries in females, and, to a lesser extent, the suprarenal (adrenal) glands all secrete androgens (including testosterone) and estrogens.

Adrenal and Suprarenal glands

These are the two suprarenal glands are located above the kidneys. Each has two parts: an outer covering, the adrenal cortex, and an inner core, the adrenal medulla. Both influence the body's responses to stress. For example, in response to a stressful situation, the pituitary gland may release beta endorphin and ACTH, which, in turn, prompt the suprarenal cortex to release hormones. Meanwhile, the autonomic nervous system stimulates the suprarenal medulla to secrete hormones such as epinephrine into the bloodstream.

The adrenals are glands just above your kidneys and their function is to regulate hormones. The outer cortex secretes hormones vital to life called corticosteroids. There are two corticosteroids: cortisol and aldosterone. Cortisol is responsible for responding to stress and is also involved in carbohydrate, fat and protein metabolism. Aldosterone is responsible for the regulation of the salt/water balance in the body. The inner adrenal medulla secretes non-essential hormones like adrenaline and noradrenaline.[107]

---

[107] https://www.gaia.com/article/how-yoga-can-help-you-recover-adrenal-fatigue

Adrenal Fatigue

This is a term you may have heard thrown around, but how do you know if this applies to you? Do any of these symptoms sound familiar to you?

- You feel tired for no reason.

- You are overwhelmed by moderate tasks

- You get more impatient and irritable than usual.

- You have trouble getting up in the morning.

- You feel rundown.

- You frequently get sick or get ill and have trouble recovering.

- You crave salty foods.

- You feel more awake than normal after the sun sets.

- You gain weight around the belly.

- You suffer from PMS more than most women.

If these symptoms sound familiar than you may have a fatigued adrenal system likely caused by stress. The hormones are involved in response to the 'fight or flight' mechanism can help the body deal with stressful situations.

Now, usually these glands are meant to deal with short bursts of stress so they can recover quickly. For example, way back when we were hunted down by wild animals, adrenaline and noradrenaline would kick in to get us away from a hungry lion, which was a real life-threatening situation.

This would usually take a few minutes followed by some recovery time in a safe shelter. However, today, the body cannot distinguish between the stress of fearing for our life from the primal 'lizard brain' and the stress we encounter in our lives today, such as road rage. Unfortunately, stress these days is more constant and taxing on our adrenals because there is no natural outlet. When we get in fight or flight we simply can not literally just run away to put the hormones to use! Most of the time that we encounter stressors it is in work or relationship situations, financial problems, family or health problems. Our adrenals again, don't know we are not in impeding danger so they constantly secrete hormones because they 'think' we are in life-threatening situations. These hormones have other functions though, like regulating metabolism and keeping your weight in check, regulating blood pressure and secreting and regulating other hormones that influence PMS.

Unfortunately, once the adrenals are fatigued they can no longer fulfill these positive functions and we start feeling tired, rundown and get sick. They simply cannot keep up the supply that is demanded and become depleted.

This is where yoga comes in to play to restore the adrenals and to actively, physically deal with stress. Yoga is a great for adrenal healing in many ways, physically and mentally.

Meditation and slow, restorative or yin movements are great ways to slow down the heart rate and shift the body from the sympathetic 'fight or flight' mode into the parasympathetic 'rest and digest' mode. To calm the body and mind, restorative yoga poses can work wonders.

Chapter 12

The Mind Body Spirit Connection

The Three Granthis , the Knots of Illusion

Granthis are the energy knots or blocks in our personality where the energy and consciousness interact and manifest in a particular way. Granthi, or knot, refers to each of the three common 'blockages' in the central pathway of the central channel of energy in the body. This central channel is calle drhe sushumna-nadi. These three knots prevent the free flow of Prana along chakras and prevent the arising of kundalini, the awakening of the life force of Prana.

According to the yogic tradition, there are three granthis:

- Brahma Granthi, the First knot. It is the lowest knot covering the area of muladhara & svadhisthana chakras. It is also known as perineal knot. The first knot is created by our attention becoming entangled with matter and materialism.It starts from Muladhara, moves up to the left channel and created superego. By its action we lose sight of the Spirit.To overcome it we should put our attention on the Spirit and not on worldly matters.[108]

- Vishnu Granthi is the Second knot. It covers the area between Manipura 3rd , Anahata, 4th, and 5th Vishuddha chakras. It is also

---

[108] https://sahajapower.wordpress.com/2011/09/17/the-three-granthis-knots-of-illusion/

known as the navel knot. **The second knot is the one by which we think and believe that we can 'do' something and achieve something in this world, with our ego.** The more we think and strive and live with out ambition and worldly desires, the more its action moves up to the right side, creating more ego. **Human beings cannot break the second knot, only Spirit/Source/God can do it.** So here we must respect ourselves and surrender ourselves to God.

- Rudra Granthi: is knotted between the 4th Anahata chakra and Ajña 5th chakra. The third and last knot occurs on the central channel due to artificiality in seeking. **The attractiveness of heart centered action and the experience of serving others can distract the yogi who desires to 'Be Love', not just experience it. Serving others is a completely satisfactory way to spend your life.**[109] However, we have to be truthful and honest in our seeking, absolutely on the Truth.

In summary, when we are seeking the Spirit, we are seeking to become one with the Spirit alone. All of our attention should go on the Spirit and should not be frittered away on nonsensical things.

Top Mind Body Spirit Activities To Implement

Let's take a look at the top Mind Body Spirit tools to implement. Admit it, we all love a top 10 list; we take quizzes, BFF tests, online questionnaires, so why not have one that is really meaningful as to complete this book as a final wrap up? So you may ask, where do I begin?

---

[109] https://jivamuktiyoga.com/fotm/untying-knots-bind-us/

For the Mind:

Make a place on your daily schedule to be still. Every single day. Whether you choose to add any other practices to your sitting time, that is up to you. Start with a 1 minute timer and work up to 5 minutes. Pick a regular time each day to sit. Hold yourself accountable and do not cancel on yourself. We sometimes, especially with women, do not add value to the Self time we place on our calendar, and we let others run into that time. Make your Self time as important as a day with your BFF.

For the Body:

Start with one simple change at at time. Implement this one thing this month! Stick to this one thing until it is a part of your life. Whether this is regarding working out, yoga practice, eating clean, making dinner at home or whatever it is, stay with it and do not overwhelm yourself with trying to do too many things at once. Choose your movement activity and aim to get moving at least 3-4 times a week for 20 minutes to begin. Most importantly find a buddy!

For the Spirit:

Find, remember or create some practices that make you feel connected to something greater than yourself.

This connection is felt by reading a spiritual text, listening to inspiring music, chanting mantra, using your mala beads, utilizing crystals and many more ways.

Set up a small altar space so you have a place to be. This can be as little as a teacup or as large as you would like it to be! Collect items that make bring you true Joy!

For the Home:

Let go of every item that is not immediately serving you or that you do not have immediate plans to use. Donating to charity is a great way to feel good about letting go! Hire an organizational specialist to help you with clutter and efficiency. Look at some design concepts that bring you happiness and begin to implement these ideas, cutting out the things that do not flow with your ideal space. See if some of the ideals of Feng Shui resonate with you. Hire someone to bless your home, or clear it yourself with sage, anointed oils and/or Reiki.

Give yourself permission to not have to save the items that you were handed down or that were given to you. Sentiment (or guilt for releasing it) is not an ideal reason to hang onto things that simply gather dust or stay in your attic or garage or clutter your living space. Only keep things that bring you true joy!

There are many people that are in your circle that may be willing to partner with you or hold you accountable to these ideals. If you want someone to help with these processes consider hiring a life, business or nutrition coach or join an accountability group on social media. With these simple living tools you can take just a few and begin there!

Remember to start somewhere, anywhere, and I trust you have, or will have, embodied many of the tools presented in this book... just not all at once. If you apply just one tool per month in a year you have implemented twelve tools, and in fiv years you have made almost fifty positive To make that one change you must simply immediately just start!

Namaste.

About the Author

Lisa Ware is a Yoga Instructor, Reiki Master, health, life and business coach. She is a happy wife and a mom living in rural Texas on their beautiful retreat center property with their dogs, cats, horses and chickens.

Her mission is to create tools to connect to the highest good for ourselves and our planet through Christ Consciousness.

Peace, Love and Light.

Full bio at www.yoga4love.com/about-lisa-ware/

Connect on Social Media

@yoga4lovelisa